1970

University of St. Francis
GEN   595.15 M274
Mann
Leeches Hirudinea their stru

3 0301 00021597 6

Y0-AFI-115

This book may be kept

*INTERNATIONAL SERIES OF MONOGRAPHS ON
PURE AND APPLIED BIOLOGY*

Division: **ZOOLOGY**

GENERAL EDITOR: G. A. KERKUT

VOLUME 11

LEECHES (HIRUDINEA)

Their Structure, Physiology, Ecology and Embryology

OTHER TITLES IN THE SERIES ON PURE AND APPLIED BIOLOGY

ZOOLOGY DIVISION

BIOCHEMISTRY DIVISION

BOTANY DIVISION

MODERN TRENDS
IN PHYSIOLOGICAL SCIENCES DIVISION

PLANT PHYSIOLOGY DIVISION

LEECHES (HIRUDINEA)

Their Structure, Physiology, Ecology and Embryology

by

K. H. MANN

DEPARTMENT OF ZOOLOGY
THE UNIVERSITY
READING

With an appendix on the Systematics
of Marine Leeches

by Prof. E. W. KNIGHT-JONES

PERGAMON PRESS

NEW YORK · OXFORD · LONDON · PARIS

1961

LIBRARY
College of St. Francis
JOLIET, ILL.

PERGAMON PRESS INC.
122 East 55th Street, New York 22, N.Y.
1404 New York Avenue N.W., Washington 5 D.C.

PERGAMON PRESS LTD.
Headington Hill Hall, Oxford
4 & 5 Fitzroy Square, London W.1

PERGAMON PRESS S.A.R.L.
24 Rue des Ecoles, Paris V^e

PERGAMON PRESS G.m.b.H.
Kaiserstrasse 75, Frankfurt am Main

Copyright © 1961
PERGAMON PRESS LTD.

Library of Congress Card Number 61–17953

Set in Imprint 11-on-12 pt. and printed in Great Britain by
THE BAY TREE PRESS, STEVENAGE, HERTS.

595.15
M274

TO MY PARENTS

$2488

"Among the numerous tribes of lower animals distributed throughout the universe, none has attracted equal notice perhaps as the Leech, and that from the periods of the most remote antiquity. Its form, its motions, its habits, are well adapted to excite the curiosity of the illiterate beholder, and, above all, its utility in alleviating the afflictions of mankind have gained a distinction for it which is denied to all the rest.

Though widely known of old, in general, the detailed investigation of the history of the Leech has been reserved for the latest era of scientific observers, and the most advanced state of science.

Doubtless the noted peculiarities of the Medicinal Leech led to the study of others, whether from the motives of mere curiosity or from the hopes of finding them endowed with similar properties. Such expectations, however, have been disappointed; for among a genus, abounding sufficiently in the variety of its species, I believe that no one is yet discovered which can be so satisfactorily employed in relieving human distress.

It is true that in this country there are leeches that will suck the blood, and eat the flesh of animals; and that in some distant regions others prove a kind of pest to man, but none seem as yet habituated to the same office wherein the medicinal leech is so useful at home.

Independently of the practical value of this animal, wherever it can be found, certain singular facts are exposed by various species of the genus *Hirudo*, which cannot but be interesting to the physiologist, and assuredly deserve to be farther known and suitably appreciated."

Sir JOHN GRAHAM DALYELL,

"The Powers of the Creator
displayed in the Creation,"
1853, p. 1.

CONTENTS

PREFACE

In English speaking countries the leeches are a neglected group of animals. Very few zoologists study them and apart from the volume in the "Fauna of British India" series there is no book in English devoted to them. In Germany and the central European countries the Hirudinea are much better known. Autrum (1939) lists over 2500 research papers, most of them in German, and leech biology has been summarized in several extensive works.

The purpose of this volume is to present a fairly concise account of the Hirudinea at a level appropriate to the honours student of zoology at a university. It is hoped that a summary of present knowledge, particularly in the realm of physiology, will also be of value to more senior zoologists, so references to the original papers have been given where appropriate. The guiding principle in determining to what extent the text need be interrupted by references has been that work summarized in the *Hirudinea* volume of Bronns: *Klassen und Ordnungen des Tierreichs* (1936–9) should be quoted without extensive references, while results published since 1939 and here reviewed for the first time should be fully documented.

The first three chapters are intended as an introduction to the group for beginners. For this purpose it has been thought best to give a fairly thorough description of *Hirudo medicinalis* as a type species rather than an account of the group in general or comparative terms. After this there follows a chapter in which the main features of the various families are set out.

The reader whose prime interest is physiological may pass straight to Chapter 4, using the previous chapters only as a source of reference when unexplained morphological or taxonomic terms are encountered.

ACKNOWLEDGEMENTS

Professor A. Graham, Professor G. P. Wells and Dr. R. B. Clark have read various parts of the text and I am particularly grateful to them for pointing out some of the mistakes resulting from my ignorance of certain fields of physiology. Naturally they have no responsibility for the errors that remain. I also wish to thank my wife for her assistance in proof reading and Mrs. G. I. Smillie for patiently typing and re-typing the script.

Professor Knight-Jones wishes to acknowledge the help given towards the appendix on marine leeches by Dr. N. Tebble of the British Museum (Nat. Hist.) and by Dr. P. H. D. H. de Silva of the National Museum, Colombo.

CHAPTER 1

INTRODUCTION

Leeches are fascinating animals, full of strange zoological paradoxes. In what other group of the animal kingdom do we find such features as a gut with no digestive enzymes, haemoglobin circulating in the coelomic fluid and fertilization carried out by introducing the sperms through the body wall of another animal? Yet such things are quite normal among leeches and are only a few of their peculiarities.

They belong to the phylum Annelida yet in many respects they have advanced beyond the level of organization which we regard as typical of annelids. When we compare the arthropods with the annelids we notice that the arthropods usually have a smaller, fixed number of segments and this has made possible a greater mobility and agility. Leeches are the only major group of annelids to have adopted a small, fixed number of segments for their basic plan and they are certainly more agile than most other annelids.

In oligochaetes and polychaetes there is a spacious fluid-filled coelom between the gut and the body wall which serves as a hydrostatic skeleton. In arthropods, which have an exoskeleton to support the body, the coelomic spaces are very small and the blood space or haemocoel has expanded to take their place. Leeches also lack the spacious fluid-filled coelom for it has become almost filled with mesenchymatous packing tissue, leaving only a system of narrow channels in which there is a circulation of coelomic fluid.

The leech nervous system is built on the usual annelid pattern of an anterior dorsal brain with connectives running to a paired ventral nerve cord which expands in each segment to form ganglia. It is characteristic of arthropods that they have more ganglia crowded into the head region than have the annelids. Insects, for instance, have six pairs of ganglia in the head region, of which three lie dorsal to the oesophagus. Oligochaetes and polychaetes have

1

four or five, of which only one is dorsal to the pharynx and one is on the circum-pharyngeal connectives, apparently in the process of migrating dorsally. Leeches more closely resemble insects for they have six pairs of ganglia in the head, usually with two placed dorsally and one pair on the lateral connectives.

The group of annelids most closely related to the leeches is undoubtedly the oligochaetes. There is in fact a connecting link in *Acanthobdella*, a leech which has a number of clear oligochaete features, such as chaetae and a spacious coelom. Both leeches and oligochaetes have a clitellum which secretes a cocoon for the reception of the eggs. Both are hermaphrodite and have well defined gonads with their own ducts to the exterior. There are many peculiarities of the embryology of oligochaetes which are also seen in leech development. In fact, it is reasonable to regard leeches as oligochaetes which have become specialized for a blood-sucking ecto-parasitic mode of life. In the process they have lost the chaetae which earthworms use in locomotion and have developed instead a ventral sucker at each end of the body, this arrangement being better adapted to clinging to the host while sucking blood. Their gut has been modified for the storage of large quantities of blood and with the great reduction of the coelom the segmentation of the body has become obscured.

The relationship of leeches to other annelid groups is expressed in the following scheme of classification:

Phylum ANNELIDA

Class POLYCHAETA	Clitellum absent, chaetae borne on parapodia.
Class ARCHIANNELIDA	Ciliated epidermis, simplified, possibly degenerate organization.
Class CLITELLATA	Clitellum present, parapodia absent.
Order OLIGOCHAETA	Chaetae present, suckers absent, number of body segments variable.
Order HIRUDINEA	Chaetae absent, suckers present, number of body segments 33.

The adaptation of the gut of leeches to blood sucking has taken place in several ways. First there is the mechanism for piercing the tissues of the host. In one major group this consists of three muscular ridges each shaped like half a circular saw, which can be everted from the mouth and used to make a Y-shaped incision in the skin. In the other group of leeches there is a very muscular proboscis which is forced out of a pore in the base of the anterior sucker while this is held in contact with the host. This mechanism is on the whole less efficient than the former, and few leeches possessing it are able to pierce the skin of a mammal. The blood is prevented from clotting by the secretion of numerous unicellular salivary glands, and is sucked into the gut by the pumping action of a muscular pharynx.

Although leeches resemble oligochaetes in being hermaphrodite, they differ in having only a single male pore and a single female pore. Moreover, while they have but a single pair of ovaries, they normally have between ten and a hundred pairs of testes. The jawed leeches transfer sperm to another leech by means of an eversible penis, but those with a proboscis normally lack the penis and implant a spermatophore containing sperms on the body surface of another leech. After this the sperms migrate through the tissues of the recipient and make their own way to the ovary.

Leeches with a proboscis (Rhynchobdellae) have a blood system of the normal annelid plan with dorsal and ventral longitudinal vessels, but the jawed leeches (Gnathobdellae) have completely lost their blood vessels and have instead a system of coelomic sinuses in which circulates coelomic fluid containing haemoglobin.

Before an accurate description of a leech can be given it is necessary to determine the limits of the segments. The only external evidence of segmentation in most leeches is in the arrangement of the sensillae, minute whitish spots which are receptor organs for tactile and light stimuli. Earlier workers adopted a convention that the annulus on which these occurred should be regarded as the first of its segment and this convention has been followed as recently as 1941 (Bhatia) and 1945 (Miller). Castle (1900) and Moore (1900) independently proposed that the nervous system should be used as a basis for determining the limits of segments, there being a general tendency for the parts of a segment to be innervated from the ganglion of that segment and by no other nerves. On critical examination (Mann, 1953a) it appears that the method of Castle and Moore is the correct one, for the intersegmental boundaries then coincide with the intersegmental septa which are present in the embryo but are lost in the adult leech.

The earlier method of delimiting segments led to disagreement about the total number of segments present as well as about their exact limits but analysis of the nervous system has led to the conclusion that there are thirty-four pairs of ganglia in all, of which the first is presumably homologous with the pre-oral ganglion of other annelids and belongs to the prostomium. The second ganglion pair is situated on the circum-oral commissures or is fused with the first, the next four are fused into a post-oral ganglionic mass, twenty-one (normally) are distributed along the ventral nerve cords, and the last seven are fused into the ganglionic mass of the posterior sucker. The descriptions of leeches which follow are based on this analysis.

CHAPTER 2

THE MEDICINAL LEECH,
HIRUDO MEDICINALIS

> He with a smile did then his words repeat:
> And said that, gathering leeches, far and wide
> He travelled; stirring thus about his feet
> The waters of the pools where they abide.
> " Once I could meet with them on every side;
> But they have dwindled long by slow decay;
> Yet still I persevere, and find them where I may."
>
> WORDSWORTH, *Resolution and Independence*, 1802.

1. OCCURRENCE

THE medicinal leech feeds by sucking the blood of mammals or occasionally of frogs, tadpoles and small fish (Blair, 1927). It is a native of Europe and south and east Asia (Lukin, 1957) and has been introduced into North America. In Britain it was once plentiful, but in the last two hundred years has declined markedly, possibly as a result of its extensive collection for medical use. It was once thought to be extinct in Britain (Harding, 1910) but is now known to be present in various relatively undeveloped areas such as the New Forest, the Lake District, South Wales, Anglesey, and Islay, Scotland. Its opportunities for obtaining blood from mammalian hosts have been greatly reduced now that fords have been replaced by bridges and cattle are watered at troughs rather than natural ponds.

2. EXTERNAL CHARACTERS

A large specimen measures about 12 cm × 1·5 cm when fully extended, although it may contract to less than half this length. The shape of the body varies according to the amount of blood

5

in the gut; the specimen illustrated in Fig. 1 was preserved shortly after gorging itself on the author! The colour pattern is very

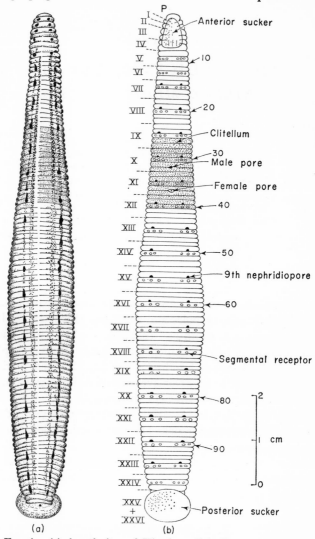

FIG. 1.   (a) dorsal view of *Hirudo medicinalis;*
(b) diagrammatic ventral view of *Hirudo medicinalis.*
The segments are numbered in roman numerals and the annuli in arabic.

variable, but in Britain usually consists of a greenish background with a pair of longitudinal red stripes and a pattern of irregular black markings nearer the lateral margins. The ventral surface is usually black with white and grey markings.

The body of the leech, exclusive of the posterior sucker, is divided by transverse furrows into 102 annuli. A typical mid-body segment comprises five annuli but towards the extremities of the body the number per segment progressively decreases. The distribution of the annuli between the prostomium and body segments is as follows:

P, I, II and XXVI ..	.. 1 annulus	..	..	total 4
III, IV and XXV ..	.. 2 annuli	..	..	total 6
V, VI and XXIV ..	.. 3 annuli	..	..	total 9
VII and XXIII ..	.. 4 annuli	..	..	total 8
VIII to XXII	.. 5 annuli	..	..	total 75
				Grand total 102

The anterior sucker is a depression on the ventral surface of segments I–IV, and at the base of the depression lies a small triradiate aperture, the mouth. The prostomium forms the anterior border of the sucker and may be turned back ventrally, thus partially closing the oral aperture. The posterior sucker is a muscular disc, approximately circular in outline, which is a more powerful organ of adhesion than the anterior sucker. It is clearly marked off from the body and is made up of seven fused segments. The anus is a very small aperture in the mid-dorsal line near the junction of the body and the posterior sucker.

The male pore lies between annuli 31 and 32, while the female pore lies five annuli further back between 36 and 37. The male pore is the more conspicuous and may be used as a guide to the position of the female pore. During the breeding season the glandular clitellum is visible on annuli 26–40. The nephridiopores are found in segment 7 between annuli 14 and 15, and between the second and third annuli of the following 16 segments. They are very small indeed, and the best way of finding them is to squeeze gently a freshly narcotized specimen, when a little fluid will be exuded from the nephridial bladders.

There are three principal kinds of sense organ on the surface of the body. Every annulus has receptor organs which in a contracted specimen may be seen to be raised on papillae. These are the annular receptors which are thought to be tactile organs. On every fifth annulus, the middle annulus of its segment, there are also white circular areas which in a preserved specimen are not raised on papillae. These contain cells which are thought to be light-sensitive. They are a convenient outward indication of internal segmentation, and are shown diagrammatically in Fig. 1. They are known as the segmental receptors, or sensillae. Finally, on segments I–V, there are five pairs of eyes which correspond in position with segmental receptors. They have larger light-sensitive cells, and are backed by a pigmented cup. They therefore appear as black dots on the head, but it may be necessary to bleach the head in 5% caustic potash before they become visible.

3. ALIMENTARY CANAL

The cavity containing the jaws, the buccal cavity, is separated from the cavity of the sucker by a low fold, the velum. When

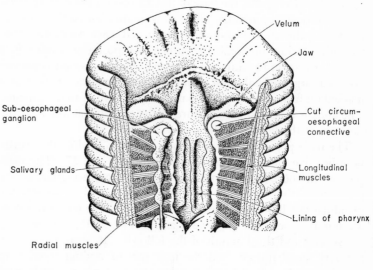

FIG. 2. Ventral dissection of the head of *Hirudo medicinalis* showing jaws protruded in biting position.

feeding, the velum is drawn back to allow the jaws to be pushed forward into the cavity of the sucker and pressed onto the skin of the host. Each jaw is a muscular ridge shaped like half a circular

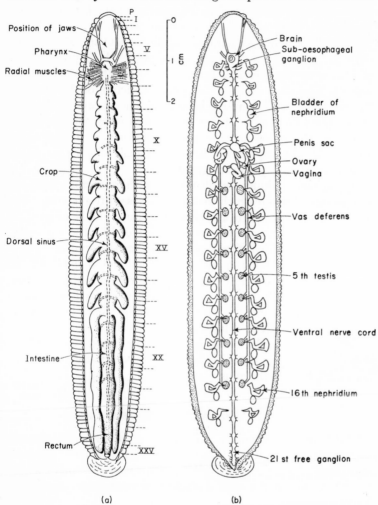

(a)   (b)

FIG. 3. (a) dissection of *H. medicinalis* to show gut. The body wall has been opened by a median dorsal incision and pinned back laterally. (b) dissection to show nephridia, reproductive organs and central nervous system. The gut has been removed and the body wall stretched laterally.

saw; one is median dorsal in position, the other two are ventro–
lateral. They have a covering of cuticle, and along the free edges
of the discs this is thickened to form a row of numerous minute
teeth. In making the incision, the muscles of the jaws rock them
so that the teeth move with a sawing action. The result is a
Y-shaped incision. Numerous unicellular salivary glands open
onto the jaws and secrete an anticoagulin which prevents the
clotting of the blood exuded from the wound. The blood is sucked
into the alimentary canal by the pumping action of the pharynx,
an oval sac about 5 mm long behind the buccal cavity. Its walls
are deeply folded when at rest, but unfold when the pharynx is
dilated by the action of the radial muscles which run out to the
body wall. The space between the radial muscles is almost
entirely occupied by salivary gland cells.

Immediately behind the pharynx is a short narrow tube, the
oesophagus, through which the blood is passed to the crop. The
crop is the largest part of the alimentary canal and is adapted for
the storage of a considerable volume of blood by the possession
of eleven pairs of diverticula, one pair in each of segments VIII–
XVIII. The last pair run back to the hind end of the body. In
segment XVIII the crop leads by a narrow pore to the intestine.
This is a thin-walled tube, slightly swollen into a heart-shaped
chamber in segment XIX, which runs straight back between the
last pair of crop diverticula to segment XXIII where it becomes
constricted and leads to the rectum. The latter, when full, is
distended to form a rectal bladder which opens to the exterior on
segment XXVI at the anus.

4. REPRODUCTIVE SYSTEM

The testes are contained in ten pairs of coelomic sacs situated
in segments XII to XXI. The number is not absolutely constant,
there may be one pair more or less. Short vasa efferentia connect
the testis sacs to the vasa deferentia of each side. These run
forward to segment XI where they become enlarged and coiled
to form storage organs known as epididymes or sperm vesicles.
Beyond these are thick-walled ejaculatory ducts which in turn lead
to a median organ, the atrium. The atrium consists of two parts,
a basal bulb covered with several layers of unicellular prostate

glands, and a penis sheath surrounding an eversible muscular penis. Spermatogonia are budded off from the walls of the testis sacs and develop into spermatozoa while floating freely in the contained coelomic fluid. They pass via vasa efferentia and vasa deferentia into the epididymes where they are stored at the begin-

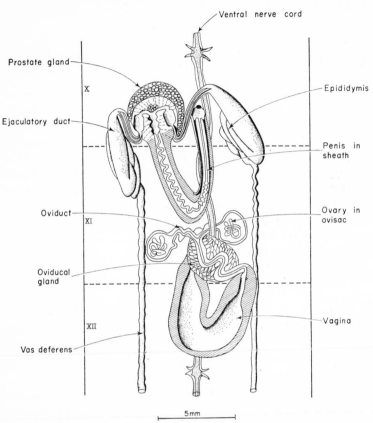

FIG. 4. Details of reproductive organs. The penis sheath, prostate bulb and female organs are shown with the dorsal wall removed. After Leuckart & Brandes, 1886–1901.

ning of the breeding season. When required for use they pass through the ejaculatory ducts to the prostate bulb where they are cemented into spermatophores. The penis is used to transfer them to the vagina of another leech at the time of copulation.

The ovaries are elongated cords with club-shaped terminations which lie freely in a single pair of coelomic sacs in segment XI. Short ducts run from these to a common oviduct, which is closely invested with a thick layer of unicellular albumen glands. The oviduct leads to a U-shaped muscular vagina which in turn opens to the exterior. Ova are budded off from the cords in the ovisacs, are fertilized by sperm received from another leech, and finally coated with albumen in the oviduct. After the cocoon has been formed by the clitellum the fertilized eggs are passed from the female pore into the cocoon, which the leech then slips over its head.

5.   EXCRETORY SYSTEM

There are seventeen pairs of nephridia opening on segments VII to XXIII. The parts of a typical nephridium are shown in Fig. 5. The outstanding feature of this nephridium compared with those of most other annelids is the complete separation of the

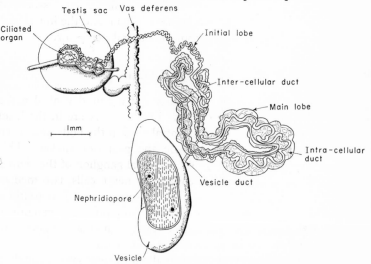

FIG. 5.   Details of a right nephridium as seen *in situ* when the body wall has been pinned out as in Fig. 3(b). After Bhatia, 1938.

funnel from the rest of the nephridium. It has become modified almost out of recognition and has become functionally a part of the circulatory system rather than of the excretory system (Bhatia, 1938). It is totally enclosed within a blood-filled sinus which lies on top of the testis sac and consists of a central capsule or reservoir which is studded with many small ciliated funnels. The reservoir is the site of formation of corpuscles of the coelomic circulatory system (see p. 15) and the cilia of the funnels beat outwards, wafting the corpuscles into the blood. The initial lobe of the nephridium lies close to this ciliated organ, but has no connexion with it. From the testis sac a winding intra-cellular canal may be followed to the main body of the nephridium. Here it joins with a network of intra-cellular canals, and these eventually lead to an intercellular canal which loops several times round the nephridium before running to the vesicle. All the glandular part of the nephridium arises from a nephridioblast cut off early from ecto-mesoderm but the vesicle and its duct to the exterior are ectodermal. The whole nephridium is closely invested with branches of the blood sinus system and excretory products are obtained from these rather than from the ciliated organ.

The first six, and the last pair of nephridia are not associated with testes. They do not have a ciliated organ, and the initial lobe ends blindly a little distance from the ventral nerve cord.

6. Nervous System

The central nervous system consists of a paired ventral nerve cord connecting 34 paired ganglia. Of these, six are in the head region, 21 are spaced along the ventral cord in the body and seven are fused into a terminal mass in the posterior sucker. This arrangement is shown in Fig. 3b. A typical ganglion of the ventral chain consists of six capsules containing nerve cells, two median ventral and the rest latero–dorsal in position, arranged round a mass of nerve fibres. In the anterior and posterior ganglionic masses there are also six capsules to each segmental ganglion and these provide the basis for analyzing each mass.

In the head region there is a (paired) supra-pharyngeal ganglion or brain lying dorsal to the pharynx at the level of segment VI and a (paired) sub-pharyngeal ganglion connected to the brain by peri-pharyngeal connectives. The distribution of cell capsules in this mass was determined by Livanow (1904) and is shown in

Fig. 6. It is seen that the first ganglion pair consists of six capsules dorsal to the gut, the second consists of three capsules on each side of the gut, while the remaining four pairs of ganglia form the ventral mass. There is an important difference between this

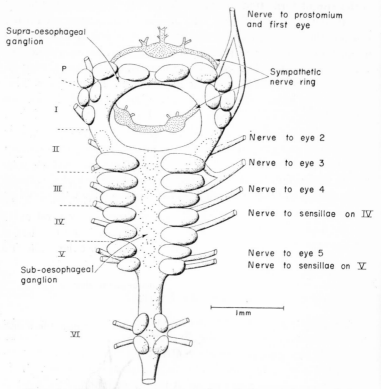

FIG. 6. Diagrammatic representation of the anterior ganglia of *Hirudo* in dorsal view showing segmental numbering of the ganglia, the capsules containing nerve cells and the roots of the anterior segmental nerves. After Livanow, 1904.

arrangement and that found in the earthworms. In the latter the cerebral ganglion is a single ganglion pair associated with the prostomium and all the ganglia of the body segments are beneath the oesophagus. In the leech one pair of segmental ganglia have migrated round the pharynx and are closely associated with the prostomial ganglia. This foreshadows the arrangement found in the Arthropoda, where several segmental ganglia contribute to the brain.

There are seven peripheral nerves in the head region, and the sense organs with which each is associated are indicated in Fig. 6. The sympathetic (= stomatogastric) nervous system consists of a nerve ring lying on the wall of the pharynx just in front of the main nerve ring, and a plexus of nerve cells and fibres on the walls of the gut (Terio, 1950). It links with the central nervous system at two points on the circum–pharyngeal nerve ring.

7. BLOOD SYSTEM

While more primitive leeches such as *Glossiphonia* have distinct blood vessels lying within the coelomic sinuses (Fig. 16), *Hirudo* has completely lost all traces of blood vessels and the blood circulates in coelomic sinuses, some of which have secondarily acquired muscular walls. There are four main longitudinal sinuses: a dorsal sinus above the gut, a ventral sinus containing the ventral nerve cord and anterior and posterior ganglionic masses, and two lateral sinuses (Fig. 7). The lateral sinuses have the muscular walls and

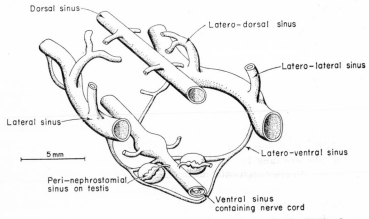

FIG. 7. Reconstruction of the coelomic sinus system of *Hirudo* from one segment in the mid body region. Original.

are responsible for circulating the blood. They give off three main pairs of branches in each segment which were named by Gratiolet

(1862): the latero–dorsals, latero–ventrals and latero–laterals. These break up into capillaries in the botryoidal tissue and the body wall, but the capillaries unite again to form tributaries of the dorsal and ventral sinuses. The detailed course of the circulation has not been worked out, but since blood is driven forward by the contraction of the lateral sinuses, there is probably a compensatory backward flow in the dorsal and ventral sinuses.

The blood consists of a plasma, coloured red by haemoglobin in solution, and containing numerous amoeboid corpuscles together with some chloragogenous cells.

8. HISTOLOGY

Under this heading are described some of the details which may be seen in transverse sections.

Epidermis

On the outer body surface is a very thin cuticle, secreted by the epidermal cells and renewed at intervals of a few days. The epidermal cells are columnar and widen at the outer ends to form pentagonal heads which fit closely against the heads of neighbouring cells. The inner ends are cylindrical and there are spaces between the cells into which penetrate blood capillaries, nerve endings, pigment cells and dermal fibres. Derived from the epidermis are various kinds of unicellular glands. On the general body surface there are two kinds of mucus glands: pear-shaped glands with the body of the cell just under the epidermis and a narrow neck opening at the surface, and elongated tubular glands which penetrate down into the muscle layers (Fig. 9). In the anterior head region all the available space between muscles is occupied by densely packed pear-shaped glandular cells whose secretion is poured on to the surface of the anterior sucker. The posterior sucker is similarly equipped. The salivary glands, which lie between the pharynx and the body wall, are modified epidermal cells. They are unicellular pyriform glands with long ductules leading to the jaws. Like the general body epidermis, the epidermis of the jaws secretes a cuticle and bears the apertures of these modified epidermal glands. In the clitellar region there are, in addition to the mucus glands, two types of gland concerned with

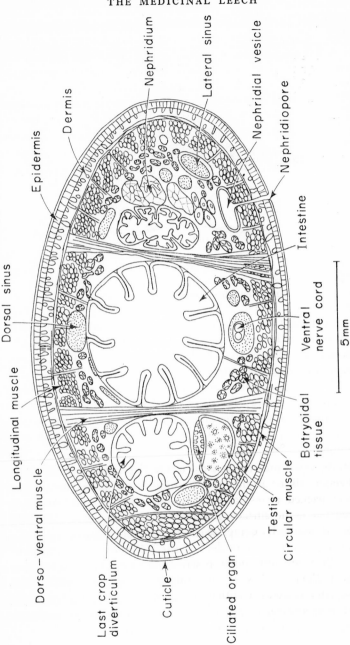

FIG. 8. Diagram of transverse section of *Hirudo* in the intestinal region. On the right hand side the section is represented as passing through a nephridiopore, on the left through a testis sac.

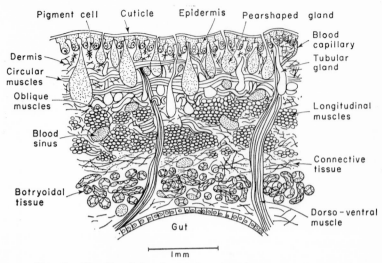

F<small>IG</small>. 9.   Details of the tissues found between the gut and the
cuticle in a transverse section of *Hirudo*.

the formation of the cocoon. The first are the chitogenous glands
which secrete the outer casing. These lie among the circular
muscles. The others are the albumen glands, which lie deeper,
among the longitudinal muscles. The sense organs of the epidermis
show several grades of complexity from simple nerve endings to
well differentiated eyes (Fig. 10). The details of these are discussed
in connexion with the physiology of the nervous system, p. 79.

Dermis

Between the epidermis and the muscle layers is a zone of fibrous
connective tissue. It consists of a ground-substance containing a
high concentration of acid muco-polysaccharide, and interlacing
connective tissue fibres. Bradbury (1958) has shown that the
fibres consist of a cortex which is probably collagenous and a
medulla which is an extension of the cell body of the fibrocyte.
He suggests that the collagen fibres are produced at the surface
of the fibrocytes. Pigment cells (brown, black, and green) are also
present in this zone. As has been mentioned above, the epidermal
gland cells penetrate into the dermis, and in highly glandular
regions may leave little room for connective tissue.

Muscles

The muscles of *Hirudo* are made up of elongated fusiform cells having an outer contractile myoplasm and an inner sarcoplasm. Immediately beneath the dermis lies a layer of circular muscle fibres, and beneath this again is a layer of oblique muscles, the

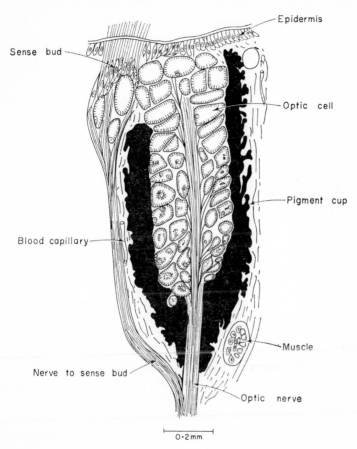

FIG. 10. Vertical section through an eye of *Hirudo* showing also a group of epidermal sense cells. After Hesse, 1897.

cells of which run at about 45° to the longitudinal axis of the body, right and left. Further towards the centre lies a thick layer of longitudinal muscle cells. Finally there are dorso–ventral bundles of fibres which are anchored beneath the epidermis and penetrate all the previously mentioned layers of muscle. Prominent dorso–ventral muscles are situated between the gut diverticula.

Botryoidal and vaso–fibrous tissue

Between the gut and the muscles of the body wall is found a tissue which is characteristic of jawed leeches and is called botryoidal tissue, from a fancied resemblance in section to bunches of grapes. It consists of a network of very fine capillary channels of the coelomic blood sinus system, lined by swollen globular cells which are heavily laden with brown pigment. The function of these is not fully understood, but they correspond in origin and

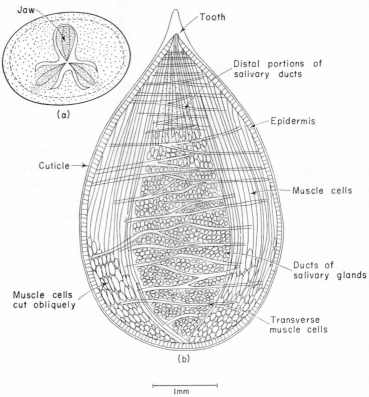

FIG. 11.   (a) plan of a transverse section through the jaws of *Hirudo*, (b) details of one jaw in section.

probably in function with the chloragogen cells of oligochaetes. The vaso–fibrous tissue consists of strands running in the connective tissue which contain deposits of brown pigment. They have a small lumen which was shown by Lankester (1880) to be continuous with that of the botryoidal tissue. It is thought that the vaso–fibrous tissue accumulates excretory products and is in some way complementary to the botryoidal tissue (Bradbury, 1959).

The Gut

The buccal cavity and pharynx of *Hirudo* are of ectodermal origin and are lined by cuticle. The pharynx has in its walls three muscular ridges which are enlarged anteriorly to form the jaws. In section each jaw is seen to have a core of closely packed salivary gland ducts, then a layer of muscle cells, and finally an epidermis surmounted by cuticle. On the cutting edge of the jaws the cuticle is thickened to form the teeth and the openings of the salivary ducts are between the teeth (Fig. 11).

The endodermal gut comprises the oesophagus, crop, intestine and rectal bladder. The wall of the crop is composed of prismatic cells having a striated border, and their cytoplasm contains numerous fat droplets. There is a crop musculature composed of interlacing muscle cells lying in connective tissue just outside the epithelium. The wall of the intestine is also a single layer of prismatic cells, but these are taller than those of the crop and lack musculature. The epithelium of the rectal bladder is ciliated. Only the tube from the rectal bladder to the anus is formed from proctodaem and has a cuticular lining.

Nervous system

The fine structure of the nervous system is discussed in Chapter 7. A transverse section of a leech usually passes through the ventral nerve cord and shows two bundles of nerve fibres together with a small median unpaired nerve known as Faivre's nerve.

CHAPTER 3

A SURVEY OF THE GROUP

(a more detailed systematic survey is given in the appendixes)

1. CLASSIFICATION

THE following is the scheme of classification adopted in this work:
Order Hirudinea
    Suborder Acanthobdellae
    Suborder Rhynchobdellae
        Family Glossiphoniidae
        Family Piscicolidae (= Ichthyobdellidae)
    Suborder Gnathobdellae (= Arhynchobdellae)
        Family Hirudidae
        Family Haemadipsidae
    Suborder Pharyngobdellae
        Family Erpobdellidae
        Family Trematobdellidae
        Family Semiscolecidae

THE ACANTHOBDELLAE comprises the single genus *Acanthobdella* which is in many ways intermediate between the Oligochaeta and the Hirudinea. Chaetae are present in five anterior segments, there is no anterior sucker, and the coelom is not entirely obliterated. *Acanthobdella* is a small fish parasite from Lake Baikal (Fig. 12).

THE RHYNCHOBDELLAE are jawless and are those leeches which utilize a proboscis to penetrate the tissues of the host. There are distinct blood vessels in the body and the blood is colourless. They are marine and freshwater forms, none is terrestrial. The group is divided into two families: the Glossiphoniidae which are dorso–ventrally flattened leeches confined to freshwater and having an anterior sucker which is continuous with the outline of the body, and the Piscicolidae which are cylindrical mostly marine leeches, having an anterior sucker which is bell shaped and clearly marked off from the body.

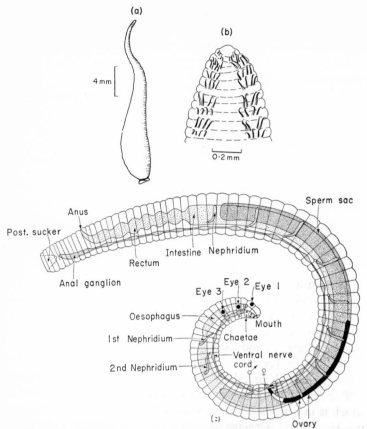

Fig. 12.   (a) general appearance of *Acanthobdella;*
            (b) details of anterior region showing chaetae;
            (c) diagram of anatomy of *Acanthobdella.*
All after Livanow, 1906.   (c) reproduced from Grassé, 1959.

2.   GLOSSIPHONIIDAE

The characters of a typical glossiphoniid leech are illustrated
by *Glossiphonia complanata*, a common European, Asian and
American species which sucks the body fluids of aquatic snails.
A typical segment has three annuli, there being only 68 annuli in
front of the posterior sucker. There are three pairs of eyes
arranged in two parallel rows, and two lines of dark pigment,

regularly interrupted by papillae bearing sense organs. On the ventral surface the posterior sucker is clearly marked off from the rest of the body, but the anterior sucker is only a small depression

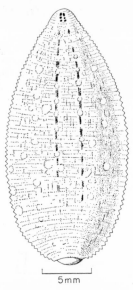

5mm

FIG. 13.   Dorsal view of *Glossiphonia complanata*.

on the under side of the head. The male pore is between annuli 25 and 26, and the female between 27 and 28. The general arrangement of the internal organs is shown in Fig. 14. The proboscis and proboscis sheath are of ectodermal origin, and are lined with a fine cuticle. The endodermal gut begins with the crop, which has six pairs of diverticula, the last pair being elongated and bent posteriorly. The intestine, also endodermal in origin, has four pairs of small lateral diverticula, and leads via the rectum (of ectodermal origin) to the anus which is placed dorsally, at the junction of the body with the posterior sucker.

The female reproductive system, which is the simpler, consists of two ovisacs lying lengthwise in the body in ventral coelomic lacunae. Each contains a single thread-like ovary, and the two sacs have a common opening at the female pore. The male reproductive system consists of ten pairs of spherical testes lying between the gut diverticula. Short vasa efferentia join these to a

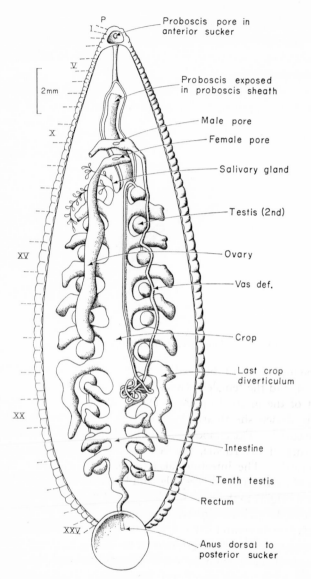

FIG. 14. Diagram of anatomy of *Glossiphonia complanata*. After Harding, 1910.

52488

LIBRARY
College of St. Francis
JOLIET, ILL.

vas deferens on each side which runs forward, loops back again, and then runs forward to meet its opposite number at the male pore. Just before the male pore the vas deferens becomes thickened and glandular, secreting the material for the formation of the spermatophores.

Nephridia are present in segments VII–IX and XII–XXI. Each nephridium consists of (i) a ciliated funnel drawn out into two

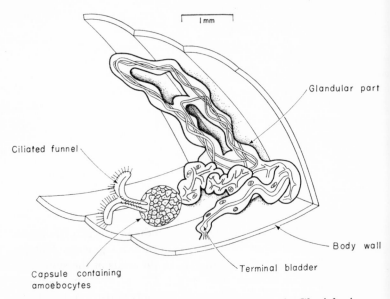

FIG. 15. Diagram showing nephridium of *Glossiphonia complanata, in situ*. After Oka, 1894.

wing-like structures, (ii) a capsule filled with amoebocytes, (iii) a looped intracellular tube, the walls of which are glandular and (iv) a bladder which opens to the exterior. The funnel opens into the ventral coelomic channel and the whole arrangement is not very different from that found in the earthworms, except that there is no continuous passage between the funnel and the glandular portion.

The coelom is not quite as restricted as in *Hirudo* and contains a separate blood vascular system. The main elements are shown in Fig. 16. There are longitudinal dorsal, ventral, and lateral sinuses, transverse subcutaneous sinuses, and various intermediate connecting sinuses. The dorsal sinus is almost completely filled

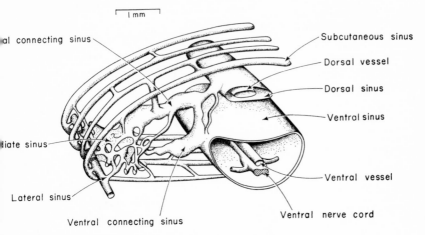

Fig. 16. Reconstruction of part of the coelomic sinus system of *Glossiphonia complanata*. After Oka, 1894.

by the dorsal contractile blood vessel; the ventral contains the ventral nerve cord, the ventral vessel, and the female genital organs, as well as the funnels of the nephridia in certain segments. Chloragogenous cells are present, adhering to the walls of the sinuses or floating freely in the coelomic fluid. The parenchyma between the coelom and the body wall contains many conspicuous adipose cells and pigment cells.

The dorsal blood vessel is equipped with fifteen sets of valves and by its contraction drives blood forward. A number of capillaries connects the dorsal and ventral vessels anteriorly, so that blood is forced backwards through the ventral vessel. It then travels through the capillaries of the posterior sucker, and up into the dorsal vessel again. In the region of the intestine the dorsal vessel has four pairs of lateral caeca which lie very close to the intestinal caeca.

Other members of the Glossiphoniidae include parasites of fish, water birds, reptiles and Amphibia. *Hemiclepsis marginata* (Fig. 17) is chiefly a fish parasite, although it may also attack tadpoles and

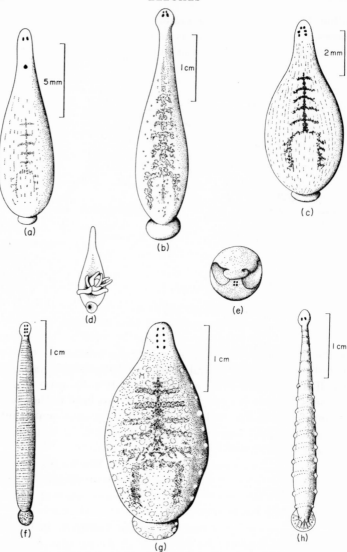

FIG. 17.   (a)–(g) various Glossiphoniidae.   (h) a piscicolid
leech.   (a) *Helobdella stagnalis;*   (b) *Hemiclepsis marginata;*
(c) *Glossiphonia heteroclita;*   (d) ventral view of *Helobdella*
carrying   young;   (e) *Glossiphonia*   after   rolling   into a ball;
(f) *Theromyzon tessulatum* starving;   (g) *T. tessulatum* after a
meal;   (h) *Piscicola geometra.*

certain molluscs. It is found through most of Europe and Asia. *Theromyzon* is a worldwide genus; members of most species enter the nostrils of wading and swimming birds and feed from the mucous membrane. *Placobdella* (= *Haementeria*) is another widely distributed genus and includes parasites of crocodiles, water turtles, frogs and fishes. *Helobdella*, on the other hand sucks the body fluids of invertebrates such as snails and insect larvae. It is really a specialized predator rather than a parasite, as it normally kills the host.

3. PISCICOLIDAE

The characters of a typical piscicolid leech are illustrated by *Branchellion torpedinis*. Both anterior and posterior suckers are clearly marked off from the body, which is divided into two distinct regions. These are the short, narrow anterior portion which includes the clitellum and the genital pores, and the longer and wider posterior portion which bears gills on the lateral margins. As in *Glossiphonia*, a complete mid-body segment has three annuli and the middle one bears, in addition to sensillae, a pair of lateral pulsatile vesicles which help to circulate the coelomic fluid through the gills. The anterior sucker bears six eyes arranged in an arc across the dorsal surface of segment IV. In a mature specimen segment XII is lifted into a fold which lies over the preceding two segments and covers the genital pores. It has been likened to the prepuce which covers the glans penis of a mammal and is often given that name.

The arrangement of the internal organs is shown in Fig. 18. The proboscis is followed by an oesophagus that bears a pair of oesophageal diverticula. The crop has six pairs of diverticula, of which all but the first pair are bilobed. The last pair of diverticula are continued back to the hind end of the body. They lie ventral to the intestine and so are almost completely hidden in dorsal view. They anastomose at five points, as shown in Fig. 18c. The intestine has four large pouches on either side and leads to the rectum by way of a ciliated chamber bearing a pair of highly folded diverticula.

There are five pairs of testes lying between the crop diverticula; the general arrangement of the reproductive organs is of the

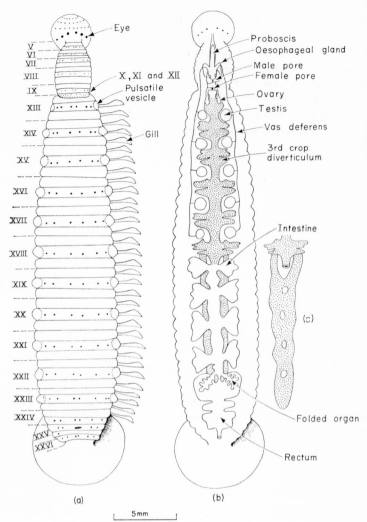

FIG. 18. *Branchellion torpedinis:* (a) dorsal view with gills removed and segments labelled on left hand side; (b) diagram of gut and reproductive system; (c) detail of the posterior crop diverticula showing fusion in five places. After Sukatschoff, 1912.

typical leech pattern. The clitellar glands are particularly developed in the Piscicolidae and in *Branchellion* take up all the space between the gut and the body wall in segments X–XII.

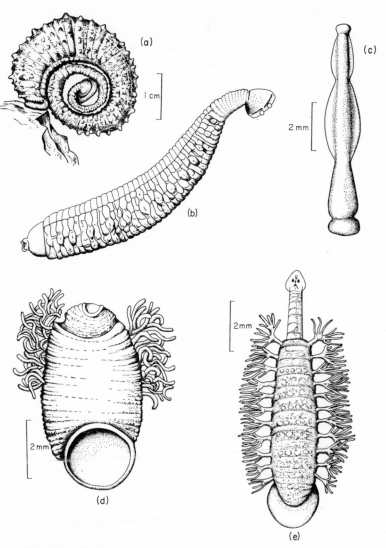

FIG. 19. Various Piscicolidae. (a) *Pontobdella muricata* in characteristic resting position; (b) *P. muricata* showing general body form, with the posterior sucker much contracted; (c) *Pterobdella amara;* (d) *Ozobranchus branchiatus;* (e) *Ozobranchus jantzeanus.* ((a) after Harding, 1910; (c) after Kaburaki, 1921; (d) after MacCallum and MacCallum, 1918; (e) after Oka, 1922).

Other Piscicolidae which may be mentioned are *Piscicola* (Fig. 17) a parasite of freshwater fishes, *Pontobdella* (Fig. 19) which attacks marine fishes, particularly elasmobranchs, and *Abranchus* which has been found on shore fishes round many parts of the North Atlantic. Our knowledge of marine fish parasites is very fragmentary, owing to the difficulty of obtaining material.

4. GNATHOBDELLAE

Turning to the Gnathobdellae, the jawed leeches, there is little to be said about the anatomy of members of the family HIRUDIDAE, since *Hirudo*, a typical and widespread form, has been fully described. Although *Hirudo* has been introduced to North America, the most common blood-sucking parasite of mammals in that country is *Macrobdella decora*. In India and adjacent countries Hirudidae abound in swamps, rice fields, etc., and there are several abundant forms, including *Hirudo* and *Hirudinaria*, which pierce the skin of the body or limbs, and *Limnatis* which enters the mouth of men and animals while drinking. Some members of this family such as *Haemopis* have weak jaws and blunt teeth and have abandoned the blood sucking habit in favour of a carnivorous mode of life. *Haemopis sanguisuga* of Europe and *Haemopis marmoratis* of North America are typical examples. They spend a good deal of their time out of water and feed on earthworms, insects, molluscs, or decaying flesh of any kind. The crop has lost most of its diverticula and *Haemopis* resembles in this the members of the family Erpobdellidae.

The outstanding characteristic of the HAEMADIPSIDAE is that they have become better adapted to terrestrial life than any other kind of leech. They are blood-sucking forms which attack man and animals, lurking on vegetation in damp places. They are particularly abundant in South East Asia. One of the chief problems confronting leeches on land is the need to keep the sucker sufficiently moist to enable it to function properly. The Haemadipsidae have achieved this by arranging that the first pair of nephridia open onto the anterior sucker and the last pair open onto membranous folds of the posterior body wall, the auricles, which are in

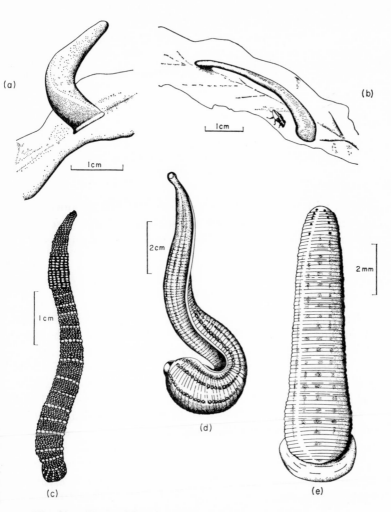

Fig. 20.   Various Gnathobdellae and Pharyngobdellae (a) and
(b) *Haemadipsa*, from photographs of living specimens; (c)
Erpobdella octoculata; (d) *Whitmania laevis;* (e) *Praobdella
büttneri*. ((a) and (b) from photographs by Gert Heinrich reproduced in Scriban and Autrum, 1934; (d) after Whitman,
1886; (e) after Blanchard, 1896.)

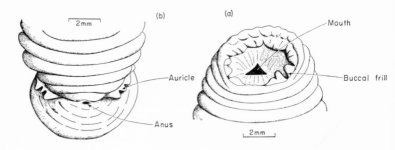

FIG. 21. (a) anterior end of *Haemadipsa* in ventral view to show buccal frill; (b) posterior end of *Haemadipsa* in dorsal view to show auricles.

contact with the posterior sucker (Fig. 21). The products of the nephridia are used to moisten the suckers, and are conserved by special frills and muscular rims on the suckers themselves.

5. PHARYNGOBDELLAE

The ERPOBDELLIDAE, sometimes known as the worm-leeches, are freshwater or amphibious leeches which have lost the power of penetrating the tissues of a host and sucking blood. The pharynx has muscular ridges homologous with those in the Hirudidae, but no jaws or teeth. These leeches are carnivorous and worms, insect larvae, etc., are swallowed whole. The gut is simple and without diverticula. The plan of the reproductive system is fairly typical, except that the testes are concentrated in the posterior one third of the body and are very abundant. *Erpobdella octoculata* is common in freshwater habitats of Europe and Asia, and is truly aquatic. In North America the corresponding leech is *Erpobdella punctata*. *Erpobdella* has five annuli per segment, but other members of the family have one or more of these annuli subdivided. Thus *Dina*, which is represented in both the Old and New Worlds has the last annulus of each segment divided into two. This tendency is carried furthest in *Trocheta* where the typical condition is three wide and five narrow annuli per segment, but further subdivision may lead to eleven annuli per segment. *Trocheta* spends a great deal of its time out of water, and in Europe is often dug up in gardens where it feeds on the earthworms.

The TREMATOBDELLIDAE and the SEMISCOLECIDAE merit only a mention in passing. The former are similar to Erpobdellidae in general structure, but have a duct from the mid gut to the body wall. The latter are perhaps intermediate between the Hirudidae and the Erpobdellidae, as they have only a single dorsal jaw rudiment and very small crop caeca. The testes are frequently subdivided. Opinions differ about whether they should be placed in the Gnathobdellae or the Pharyngobdellae.

CHAPTER 4

NUTRITION

1. IN HIRUDIDAE

THE nutrition of leeches is of interest for several reasons. One is that typical leeches are blood-sucking ectoparasites and they are remarkably adept at removing from the host a very considerable quantity of blood without being noticed. This requires sharp, precise cutting equipment and the assistance of a local anaesthetic. Secondly, the blood must be prevented from clotting in the gut, for during locomotion the leech becomes alternately short and thick and long and thin and this would be impossible if the gut contained a mass of clotted blood. Finally, a series of investigators failed to identify any proteolytic enzymes in the gut of *Hirudo* and it appears that the function of digestion has been taken over entirely by symbiotic bacteria.

The jaws of *Hirudo* have been described in an earlier section (p. 8). As soon as they begin to saw into the tissues of the host a secretion from the salivary glands is poured into the wound. It has long been known that an extract of the head of *Hirudo* contains a powerful anticoagulin (Haycraft, 1884) which was given the name of hirudin and the presence of this substance was thought to account for the fact that a wound made by a leech bleeds freely for a very long time. However, Lindemann (1939) collected some blood from such a wound and found that its clotting time was normal. He found that leech head extract also contains a histamine-like substance capable of causing the dilatation of capillaries so he postulated that this was the substance actually injected into the wound and that the free flow of blood was due to the enlargement of the blood vessels rather than the inhibition of clotting. He suggested that the act of biting and the secretion of the salivary glands is divisible into two phases (i) the biting phase, when the incision is being made and the histamine-like compound is being injected

36

and (ii) the sucking phase when the blood flowing past the jaws is mixed with a secretion containing hirudin which prevents the blood coagulating in the crop. On the other hand, Stammers (1950) found that the blood flowing from a wound made by the land leech *Haemadipsa* had an abnormal coagulation time for some 8 minutes after the leech withdrew its jaws, so presumably a certain amount of hirudin was injected into the wound. It therefore seems likely that an anticoagulant is produced by all blood-sucking leeches but that not all of them inject this substance into the wound on the host. Some at least rely on a histamine to maintain a free flow of blood and use the anticoagulant to prevent the meal of blood from clotting during storage in the crop. Hirudin was prepared in pure form and analysed by Yanagisawa and Yokoi (1938). They showed that it is an hydrolysis product of protein with an empirical formula $C_{30}H_{60}O_{20}N_8$ and a molecular weight of 852. It probably acts by inhibiting the thrombokinase (Lenggenhager, 1936). Only 0·8 mg is required to prevent indefinitely the coagulation of 5 ml of rabbit blood. Lenggenhager also pointed out that one may apply tincture of iodine to a leech wound without feeling any pain, indicating that the saliva also has a local anaesthetic effect, but the substance responsible has not been identified.

It is a general character of blood-sucking leeches that they feed infrequently but take large quantities of blood at one time. *Hirudo* normally takes two to five times its own weight of blood and *Haemadipsa*, the land leech, may take ten times its own weight. These large meals are digested slowly over a period of many months. Pütter (1907, 1908) drew up detailed balance sheets for *Hirudo*. A typical example, quoted in dry weights, runs as follows: a leech of 128 mg took in 640 mg during one meal. The digestion of the meal took about 200 days and during that time there was a loss in weight by excretion of 524 mg. The balance of 116 mg had been incorporated into the tissues of the leech and as no further meal was taken the leech lived on its reserves for another 100 days. From this it is apparent that a leech will grow steadily if it obtains a meal every six months and that it will not die of starvation if it feeds only once per year. As one would expect, Pütter found that the leech derives most of its energy from protein breakdown so long as it has blood in its crop; he estimated the energy consumption

as 15 cal per day at 18°C. During starvation the leech utilized
the stored carbohydrates and fats and its energy consumption
dropped to about 7 cal per day.

When a meal of blood has been sucked into the crop it first
thickens, water being abstracted and passed out via the nephridia
together with considerable quantities of sodium chloride. Worth
(1951) reported that when land leeches are feeding they become
surrounded by a pool of clear fluid. This is presumably a nephridial
excretion. In Fig. 22 is shown that in *Hirudo* the weight of blood

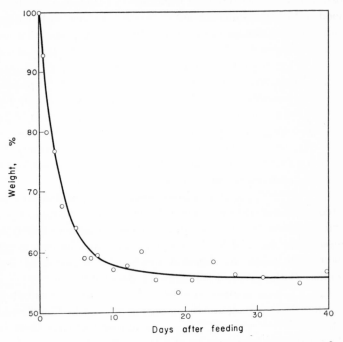

FIG. 22. Reduction in weight of *Hirudo* due to excretion of
water after feeding. Drawn from data in Büsing *et al.*, 1953.

in the crop decreases by more than 40% in ten days. The haemoglobin soon becomes deoxygenated but the erythrocytes remain
intact for a very long time. So remarkable is the freedom from
putrefaction that intact erythrocytes have been found 18 months
after ingestion and even white corpuscles and pathogens may be

identified after many weeks in the crop. A digestive system which produces such a slow, controlled haemolysis is clearly unusual and several attempts have been made to identify the enzymes concerned and to settle the question of whether digestion takes place

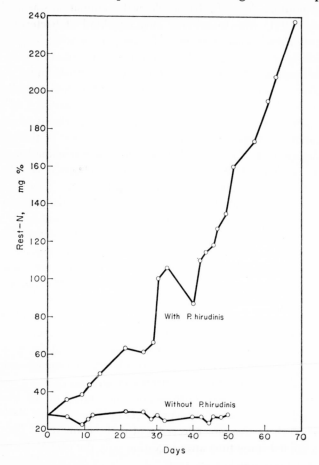

Fig. 23.   Change in Rest-Nitrogen content of blood kept with and without *Pseudomonas hirudinis*. From Büsing *et al.*, 1953.

in the crop or in the intestine. Diwany (1925) injected milk, egg-proteins and peptones into the gut of starving *Hirudo* but found that none was digested and the leeches continued to lose weight.

Graetz and Autrum (1935) failed to find any proteolytic enzymes in extracts of *Hirudo* gut wall. They suggested that digestion depends on bacterial decomposition, but this is difficult to reconcile with the observation that the corpuscles remain unchanged for many months. A careful bacteriological examination was made by Büsing (1951) who found that only one kind of bacterium was present, *Pseudomonas hirudinis*. Its properties were investigated by Büsing *et al.* (1953). They were first concerned to show that it was capable of digesting blood protein, transforming it into soluble nitrogenous compounds. They therefore took two samples of sterile defibrinated sheep's blood and inoculated one with *P. hirudinis*. In subsamples taken at intervals the protein was separated by coagulation and the nitrogen content of the residue was determined. In the sterile blood the figure remained approximately constant at 25–28 mg% but in the inoculated samples the figure rose to over 200 mg% in 65 days (Fig. 23). This indicates a progressive breakdown of protein during the whole period and shows that the bacterium is capable of digesting blood at the slow rate normally found in leeches. To complete the picture Büsing *et al.*, showed that *P. hirudinis* can also break down fats.

When an antibiotic, chloromycetin, was injected into the crops of leeches, further digestion was inhibited. When *P. hirudinis* was added to a culture of *Staphylococcus aureus* in sheep's blood the *Staphylococcus* was eliminated, suggesting that the *Pseudomonas* has the ability to prevent the development of other bacteria. This would account for the freedom from putrefaction of the blood in the crop. Presumably the pseudomonads are well mixed with the meal of blood when it comes into the crop, eliminate any organisms which might cause putrefaction and slowly attack the red blood cells one by one. The products of digestion are absorbed by the leech as they are released and if the contents of the crop are examined some time after ingestion only the corpuscles which have not been attacked are seen.

It is likely that the problem of ensuring that pseudomonads are present in the crop of every leech is met by arranging that during the process of cocoon formation, when the leech is forming the plugs of the cocoon with its mouth, it passes some of the pseudomonads into the nutritive fluid surrounding the eggs, for it is known that the young leeches have *P. hirudinis* in their guts before they leave the cocoon. The extraordinary picture with which we are presented of an animal handing over the whole of its digestive processes to symbiotic bacteria has few if any parallels in the animal kingdom (perhaps the nearest are those mammals and insects which rely on micro-organisms for the digestion of cellulose), yet it is an arrangement which enables the leech to store a supply of food for a very long period and to receive a steady supply of soluble nitrogenous compounds. It is capable of evolving slowly from the more normal arrangement, the leech producing progressively fewer enzymes and relying more and more on the bacteria; since it enables the leech to make its meals last longer there is an obvious selective advantage.

The site of absorption may be the crop, the intestine, or both, but the intestine is much more vascular and it would be surprising if it did not play some part in absorption. During digestion the haemoglobin is split into its component parts globin and haematin and the latter into proto-porphyrin and inorganic iron. It is the globin which forms a major source of nutriment for the leech. It has been reported that during assimilation there is an accumulation of glycogen and fat in the gut epithelium and since there is little glycogen in the meal of blood it is presumably synthesized from the products of protein digestion.

Turning from *Hirudo* to *Haemopis* we find that the teeth of this leech are blunt and food organisms such as earthworms and slugs are devoured whole. Studies of the digestive enzymes present (Autrum and Graetz, 1934; Graetz and Autrum, 1935) showed that enzymes for initiating protein digestion were absent, although there were several enzymes for the later stages of the process. They found a dipeptidase and a carboxypeptidase working optimally at pH 7·8, an aminopeptidase (pH 8·05) and peptone splitting factors (pH 7·6 and 8·2). Lipases were located in the intestinal wall and the body tissues. They therefore postulated that the initial stages of protein digestion were due to putrefaction, although one difficulty about this theory is that boiled earthworms were digested about as rapidly as fresh ones. All the evidence points to the existence of symbiotic bacteria as yet not isolated, which have taken over a part of the digestive process.

2. In Rhynchobdellae

Our knowledge of the nutrition of rhynchobdellid leeches is very scanty indeed. Food is obtained by inserting a proboscis into the tissues of the host. Many are fish parasites, but it is somewhat surprising that a proboscis containing no hard skeletal parts can be forced through the integument of a fish. A study of the forces involved would prove interesting. Many rhynchobdellids have a pair of diverticula between the base of the proboscis and the beginning of the crop. In *Placobdella costata* according to Reichenow (1922) the walls of the diverticula are made up of two kinds of cells, tall columnar cells and broad ones. The latter contain numerous thread-like micro-organisms and these organisms are also found in the posterior part of the crop. This leech sucks tortoise blood and in the neighbourhood of the micro-organisms the blood corpuscles were haemolysed, while elsewhere they were not. This might well be a case of digestion by symbiotic micro-organisms. On the other hand, Reichenow also suggested that symbiotic micro-organisms were responsible for digestion of blood in certain mites and insects. These were subsequently shown to have adequate gut enzymes and Wigglesworth (1953) suggested that the micro-organisms supply vitamins or other essential growth factors.

Jashke (1933) examined the oesophageal diverticula of various other rhynchobdellids including *Piscicola geometra*, *Cystobranchus respirans* and *Branchellion torpedinis*. He found that these diverticula never contained blood but were filled instead with an albuminous fluid in which were suspended large numbers of bacteria. Once again these might well be micro-organisms responsible for the digestion of blood, but their presence in the crop has not so far been detected. A systematic survey of the crop flora of leeches is much needed.

The food reserve of the rhynchobdellid leech *Glossiphonia complanata* appears to be mainly in the form of fat droplets. Adipose cells are a very prominent feature of the connective tissue and Bradbury (1956) has shown that ten weeks' starvation results in a 95% reduction in the volume of the contained droplets. Pütter (1908) found that fat metabolism is comparatively unimportant in the physiology of *Hirudo* and van Emden (1929) thought that fat was actively excreted. The marked difference between the two types of metabolism may be related to the differences in diet. While *Hirudo* is purely sanguivorous *Glossiphonia* plunges its proboscis into the tissues of a freshwater snail and after removing the liquids it may finally suck all the soft parts out of the shell.

CHAPTER 5

EXCRETION AND WATER BALANCE

1. EXCRETION

THE greater part of the food of leeches consists of proteins which during digestion are converted to amino-acids and absorbed into the body. A proportion of these amino-acids are synthesized again into proteins for use in body building but most are deaminated and used as a source of energy. Deamination results in the production of ammonia, a substance which is poisonous and readily diffusible, so it has to be excreted quickly or changed into something less toxic, such as urea or uric acid. Another source of nitrogen in the food is nucleic acid which on digestion yields purines such as adenine or guanine. These are likewise amino compounds and on deamination give hypoxanthine or xanthine, which in the presence of xanthine oxidase may be changed into uric acid. In vertebrates most of these metabolic processes take place in the liver and the end products, ammonia, urea or uric acid, are then excreted by way of the kidneys. In annelids these processes are particularly associated with the chloragogenous tissue, while the organs of excretion are the nephridia.

Chloragogen cells are modified coelomic epithelial cells which become loaded with yellow or brown material in their cytoplasm and project freely into the coelom. When fully loaded they break free and float about in the coelomic fluid. In oligochaetes and polychaetes they are concentrated in the vicinity of blood vessels, particularly those of the gut. In leeches, where blood vessels are often lacking, they line the haemo–coelomic channels and may be especially concentrated in a dense network of coelomic capillaries known as the botryoidal and vaso–fibrous tissue (see p. 20). Nitrogenous excretion has been most closely studied in earthworms and the results are worth recording as a guide to what we may expect to happen in leeches.

Various workers have made physiological observations on slices of earthworm intestine with chloragogenous tissue attached. Cohen and Lewis (1949) showed that large quantities of ammonia are found there and that arginase is present. Heidermanns (1937) found that this tissue converts peptone to urea and called the chloragogenous tissue " the central organ of urea metabolism." Bahl (1947) found, in addition to ammonia and urea, creatinine which is presumably produced by muscular tissue. Florkin (1935) showed the presence of xanthine–oxidase. These results clearly indicate that ammonia is being converted to urea by the Krebs cycle involving the production of arginine and its conversion to urea and ornithine with the aid of arginase; further, that uric acid synthesis by the oxidation of xanthine or hypoxanthine is occurring in the tissue slices. Semal-van Gansen (1956) also showed that the chloragogen cells are the site of glycogen metabolism and fat storage and contain abundant acid phosphatase. She drew attention to the similarity in function between chloragogenous tissue and vertebrate liver.

It has long been known that chloragogen cells of earthworms accumulate large numbers of yellowish refringent granules which are insoluble in acids or alkalis (except ammonia) at ordinary temperatures. Semal-van Gansen found that in *Allolobophora caliginosa* these are made up of a purine, probably a heteroxanthine such as 7-methyl xanthine, together with a chromolipid and a small amount of mica. Roots (1960) working with *Lumbricus terrestris* could find no purine. During starvation the chloragogen cells retain their granules but give up glycogen and fat droplets from the cytoplasm. It is now abundantly clear that earthworm chloragogenous tissue is the main site of deamination and storage of carbohydrates and fats. The waste products of metabolism are ammonia and urea, which are presumably liberated into the coelomic fluid, and possibly a purine which is accumulated in granular form, to be liberated into the coelom at the breaking up of the chloragogen cell. Particulate material in the coelomic fluid may be ingested by coelomic corpuscles and disposed of in various ways. It may be deposited in the body wall as pigment, deposited as brown bodies in the posterior part of the worm or carried through the epidermis to the outside (Stephenson, 1930). Cordier (1934) established that the walls of the narrow, ciliated tubes of the nephridia perform athrocytosis, i.e. the absorption of certain colloidal and other finely dispersed particles. Bahl (1947) showed how fluid passing along the nephridial tubes of *Pheretima* has its chemical composition changed (Table 1). Glucose and amino-acids are completely reabsorbed and PO_4, Cl, Na, K and creatinine

TABLE 1. RELATIVE CONCENTRATIONS OF VARIOUS SUBSTANCES
IN BLOOD, COELOMIC FLUID AND URINE OF EARTHWORMS,
AND ANALYSIS OF URINE

Constituent	Relative concentrations in:			Analysis of urine mg/100 ml.
	Blood	Coelomic fluid	Urine	
Ammonia	1·5	1	1	2·7
Creatinine	7	5·5	1	0·5
Urea	0·8	1	1	3·2
Protein	121	16	1	30 *
Na	4	8	1	23·5
K	8	2·5	1	9·2
Ca	1·4	1·8	1	12
Cl	13·5	22	1	3·7
Mg	1·4	7	1	5·4
PO_4	16	1·8	1	1·1
SO_4	2	1·4	1	1·6

* May have been derived from mucus contaminating urine.
From Bahl, 1947.

are absorbed to a considerable extent, along with water, leaving as the chief organic elements of the urine urea, ammonia and creatinine in the ratio 6·5 : 5·3 : 1. Ramsay (1949a and b) showed that earthworm urine is strongly hypotonic to the body fluids under normal conditions and that salt resorption takes place in the distal rather than the proximal part of the nephridium.

Returning to leeches, we find that there is no single tissue corresponding to the chloragogenous tissue of earthworms. Cuénot (1931) found that when ammonium carminate is injected into the coelomic fluid of rhynchobdellid leeches it is taken up by certain cells lining the coelomic channels and when injected into *Hirudo* it is taken up by the botryoidal tissue. In each case these cells normally accumulate pigmented granules and it is reasonable to assume that they correspond in part with the chloragogenous cells of other annelids. Cuénot further showed that when indigo sulphate is introduced to the coelomic cavities it is taken up by the vaso–fibrous tissue of *Hirudo* (p. 21) and by the large pigment cells in the connective tissue of rhynchobdellids. Tilloy (1937) carried the investigation further and concluded that in general the botryoidal tissue of gnathobdellids and coelomic epithelial cells of rhynchobdellids take up particles of diameter greater than 10 Å while the vaso–fibrous tissue of *Hirudo* and the pigment cells of rhynchobdellids take up those of diameter less than 10 Å.

The only histochemical investigation of these excretory tissues by modern methods is that of Bradbury (1957, 1959). He was concerned primarily with the metabolism of iron, which is an important constituent of the diet of blood-sucking leeches. The haem probably breaks down to yield first a porphyrin and then linear tetra-pyrrole compounds similar to vertebrate bile pigments. These substances have been identified in the vaso–fibrous tissue of *Hirudo* and in the large pigment cells of *Glossiphonia complanata*. Bradbury thinks that these are the sites of haem metabolism. In the case of the pigment cells of *Glossiphonia* it appears that they are derived from adipose cells which are such a conspicuous feature of the parenchyma of this leech. Tetra-pyrroles accumulate in the adipose cells until there comes a point when the cytoplasm degenerates leaving an envelope containing a mass of pigmented spheres. Previously it has been thought that these pigment cells were derived from coelomic epithelial cells or from amoebocytes but it now appears more likely that they are in fact derived from adipose cells which function as kidneys of accumulation.

Bradbury failed to identify the pigment present in the botryoidal tissue of *Hirudo*, but established that it is soluble in weak sodium hydroxide and in glacial acetic acid. He found that iron was present in the botryoidal tissue but not in the vaso–fibrous tissue. It therefore appears that during the metabolism of haem the pyrrholes pass to the vaso–fibrous tissue while the iron is stored in the botryoidal tissue. An investigation of the fate of the products of protein metabolism in leeches along the lines of that of Semal-van Gansen in earthworms, is much needed. Robin *et al.* (1957) identified a new guanidine derivative in the muscles of *Hirudo*.

They gave it the name hirudonine and suggested that it probably serves as a phosphate acceptor rather than an excretory material.

In leeches the act of phagocytosis by coelomic corpuscles has frequently been observed but the route subsequently taken by the corpuscles is less clear. Van Emden (1929) claimed that in *Erpobdella* they pass into the lumen of the intestine. Others have thought that they passed out of the epidermis or were laid down as pigment, as in earthworms. A fourth possibility is that the amoebocytes are swept up by the nephridial funnels and passed into the nephridial capsule, there to break down their waste matter and pass it into the nephridial tubules. When bacteria or carmine particles are injected into the coelom of glossiphoniid leeches they may subsequently be found concentrated in the nephridial capsules, but in most leeches there is no opening from the capsule to the rest of the nephridium, so it is difficult to see how the waste products are eliminated.

In an attempt to understand the role of the nephridial capsule we must pause to consider the structure and evolution of nephridia. In both earthworms and leeches they are metanephridia (Goodrich, 1945) consisting basically of an inner ciliated funnel leading to a coiled length of tube which opens to the exterior by way of a terminal bladder. The special structure peculiar to leeches is a capsule containing amoebocytes which is inserted between the funnel and the tubular region. The capsule is small with a single funnel in the primitive Glossiphoniidae but large with multiple funnels in the Hirudidae. The Erpobdellidae have two capsules and funnels per nephridium. Two functions have been ascribed to the capsule. One is to receive coelomic corpuscles loaded with excretory products, the other is to act as a site for the multiplication of coelomic corpuscles. In primitive leeches such as *Theromyzon* there is a communication between the cavity of the capsule and that of the tubules (Fig. 24), so it is not difficult to see that amoebocytes loaded with excretory products could break them down and discharge them into the nephridium, but in most other leeches there is a partition between the capsule and the rest of the nephridium, and waste products must either diffuse through the intervening tissue or travel via the coelomic circulation. Under these conditions it seems that the capsule has changed its function and become specialized for manufacturing coelomic corpuscles.

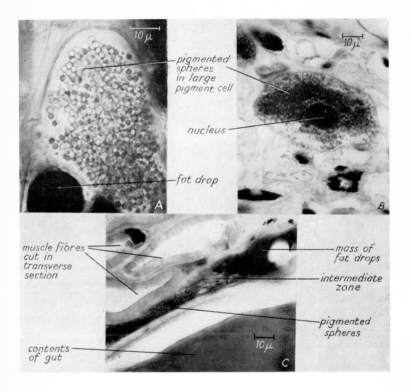

PLATE I

A, large pigment cell of *Glossiphonia complanata*, seen in a section of the lateral coelomic sinus region;

B, a similar section to that shown in A, but stained with iron haematoxylin to show the slight basiphilia of the pigmented spheres;

C, an adipose cell containing numerous pigmented spheres. The cell comprises a mass of fat drops, an intermediate zone and pigmented spheres. From Bradbury, 1957.

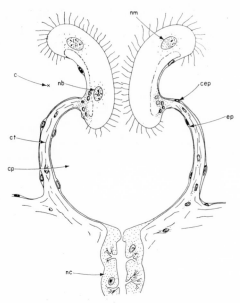

FIG. 24. Diagram of nephridial capsule of *Theromyzon*.
c, coelomic cavity of ampulla; *cep*, coelomic epithelium; *cp*,
cavity of capsule; *ct* connective tissue; *ep*, lining epithelium
of wall of capsule; *nb*, nucleus of basal cell; *nc*, nephridial canal
cell; *nm*, nucleus of marginal cell. From Goodrich, 1945.

From the work of Bradbury (1959) it seems possible that in *Hirudo*
particulate matter from the coelomic fluid is retained indefinitely
in the botryoidal tissue and not taken to the nephridia, as it is in
more primitive forms. In the Hirudidae, according to Bhatia
(1938) the cilia of the multiple funnels beat outwards and serve to
waft newly formed corpuscles into the coelomic circulation. This
being so, it follows that the urine passed out of the nephridia is
obtained entirely by filtration through the walls of the tubules and
that the material picked up by the coelomic corpuscles must either
be broken down to a soluble state or be carried to parts of the body
other than the nephridia.

The chemical composition of the urine of *Hirudo* has been
determined on a number of occasions (Heidermanns, 1937). Under
normal conditions about 72% of the nitrogen excreted is in the
form of ammonia while aminoacids, purines, urea and creatinine

each account for 5–10%. This is a much higher proportion of ammonia than is produced by earthworms and is accounted for by the presence in the nephridial capsule of bacteria which convert more complex nitrogenous compounds into ammonia. Büsing

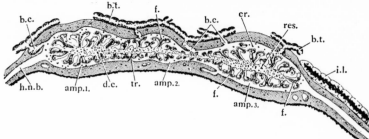

FIG. 25. Longitudinal section of nephridial capsule of *Hirudinaria* showing numerous funnels opening into a coelomic ampulla (× ca. 180). *amp*, 1, 2 and 3, three coelomic ampullae; *b.c.*, communications between ampullae and botryoidal tissues; *b.t.*, botryoidal tissue; *cr*, coelomic corpuscles; *d.c.*, dividing corpuscles; *f*, funnel of nephridial capsule; *h.n.b.*, nephridial branch of coelomic sinus system; *i.l.*, initial lobe of nephridium; *res*, reservoir of nephridial capsule; *tr*, trabeculae. After Bhatia, 1941.

et al. (1953) showed that there are two species present, *Corynebacterium vesiculare* which forms a layer like the pile of a carpet on the bladder wall (this has been mistaken for ciliation) and *C. hirudinis* which floats freely in the fluid. When urine was removed from the bladders and stored in sterile containers the ammonia content progressively increased. When leeches were treated with antibiotic

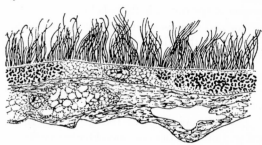

FIG. 26. Symbiotic bacteria on the wall of the nephridial bladder of *Hirudo*. From Grassé, 1959; after Jaschke, 1933.

to inhibit the bacteria there was a fall in the ammonia content of the urine. Presumably the fluid entering the nephridial vesicles contains a fair amount of urea and other complex nitrogenous compounds which are acted on by the bacteria to give a urine containing mostly ammonia.

2. WATER AND SALT BALANCE

The nephridia of leeches, in addition to their function of excreting nitrogenous waste, perform the task of maintaining water balance. There is no detailed study of this process in leeches but it is certain that the osmotic pressure of the body fluids is considerably higher than that of the water in which they live so that there must be a constant inward flow of water through the integument. The function of the nephridia is to remove the excess water while retaining as many as possible of the inorganic ions other than ammonia. It is unlikely that they are completely efficient, any more than are the nephridia of earthworms (Table 1), so there is a steady drain on the salt content of the coelomic fluid which must be replaced. A certain amount of mineral salts will be taken in with the food but Krogh (1939) showed that *Haemopis* has a salt uptake mechanism in the epidermis. He first exposed the leeches to a current of distilled water for two weeks during which time there was no opportunity to replenish the stock of salts lost in the urine. He then placed them in frog Ringer diluted to 1/100 and found that they took up chloride ions at a rate of $0.48 \, \mu M/g/h$. In order to maintain electrostatic equilibrium these ions would have to be accompanied by ions of opposite sign or exchanged against ions of the same sign. When the experiment was repeated using other salt solutions it was found that the leeches were able to take up sodium ions from sodium bicarbonate solution and chloride ions from ammonium chloride solution. Krogh therefore concluded that the leeches had separate mechanisms for the active uptake of sodium and chloride ions and that the two were normally taken up together.

Although leeches frequently leave the water to feed or to breed, they appear to have no very effective mechanism for controlling water loss. When exposed to dry air they secrete abundant mucus from the epidermis but it does not reduce water loss very appreciably. Klekowski (1961) kept *Hirudo* and *Haemopis* in air of 80% relative humidity at 22°C and found that their water content was reduced to 20% in 4–5 days, after which death ensued. If returned to the water after about 4 days they were able to return to full hydration within a few hours. A more drastic process of desiccation was carried out by Hall (1922) on the rhynchobdellid leech *Placobdella parasitica*. When a current of dry air was passed over these leeches they lost 92% of the water in the body in $7\frac{1}{2}$ hr, but recovered when placed in water at 13°C.

CHAPTER 6

CIRCULATION AND RESPIRATION

IN MOST annelids there is a well developed blood vascular system consisting of longitudinal dorsal and ventral vessels, a plexus on the wall of the gut and regular lateral segmental vessels supplying the body wall, nephridia, etc. Leeches do not conform to this pattern. The nearest approach is found in the rhynchobdellid

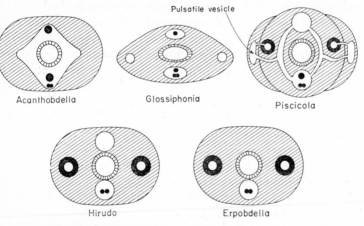

FIG. 27. Comparative diagrams illustrating the progressive loss of median dorsal and ventral blood vessels and their functional replacement by lateral coelomic sinuses with muscular walls in various leeches. Coelomic sinuses open circles; dorsal and ventral vessels solid circles; thick-walled circles indicate coelomic sinuses with muscular walls.

leeches which have small longitudinal vessels but no segmental ones. These longitudinal vessels lie in coelomic sinuses (Fig. 27) and it is the coelomic fluid which circulates to all parts of the body, carrying out gaseous exchange and transporting food materials and excreta. The blood in the longitudinal vessels is a clear fluid in which no respiratory pigment has been identified. The coelomic fluid is colourless in the rhynchobdellids but contains haemoglobin in solution in the gnathobdellids. In the latter group there is no trace of true blood vessels, not even in development. Their circulatory system consists entirely of coelomic sinuses and circulation is brought about mainly by the contraction of lateral sinuses which have acquired muscular walls.

Oxygen uptake in most leeches takes place through the general body surface, but the Piscicolidae have accessory respiratory organs filled with coelomic fluid which may be large leaf-like gills, as in *Branchellion* (Fig. 18) or small hemispherical vesicles which pulsate rhythmically (*Piscicola*, Fig. 17). When it is necessary to increase the rate of oxygen uptake *Piscicola* increases the rate of pulsation of its vesicles but other leeches ventilate the body surface by means of dorso–ventral undulations which pass along the body from head to tail. This movement is carried out while the posterior sucker is held fast to the substratum, the head moving freely, and it has been described as a swimming movement performed while standing still. The rate of ventilation or of pulsation is related to temperature in the manner shown in Fig. 28.

An alternative or supplementary method of increasing oxygen uptake is to increase the rate of pumping of the coelomic fluid round the body. Herter (1936) found that in *Erpobdella*, where it is sometimes possible to observe the lateral sinuses by transparency, the rate of pumping varied from 3·7 per min at 17°C to 17·1 per min at 27°C. The mechanism controlling pumping was studied in *Hirudo* by Gaskell (1919). From each segmental ganglion two nerves run out on each side and send branches to the walls of the lateral sinus. The anterior segmental nerves accelerate the rate of pumping while the posterior nerves cause a retardation. Contractions continue for long periods after all nerves have been severed, suggesting that the stimulus for contraction originates in the muscles of the sinus wall. Such a mechanism is called myogenic to distinguish it from one in which the stimulus originates in the nervous system, which is neurogenic. The arrangement in *Hirudo* may be compared with that in the mammalian heart, where the beat is myogenic and is accelerated by secondary sympathetic fibres but retarded by a branch of the vagus nerve. The parallel

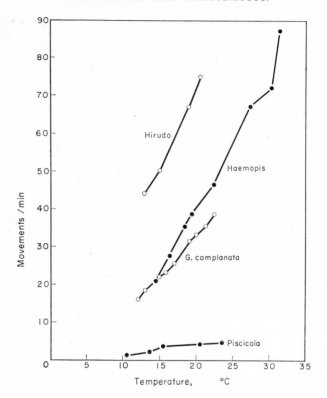

Fig. 28. Rate of making respiratory movements by various leeches at various temperatures. Redrawn from Herter, 1936–9.

is even more striking if we consider the effects of drugs. In *Hirudo* the accelerating effect of the anterior segmental nerve is abolished by ergotoxin while the slowing effect of the posterior nerve is abolished by curare. Injection of adrenalin increases the rate of pumping, while muscarin decreases it. Schwab (1949) found that adding acetylcholine to water surrounding *Erpobdella* caused speeding up which was maintained for about half an hour, after which there was a period of depression. Atropine, on the other hand, slowed the contractions. These effects are very similar to those found in mammals and indeed in many vertebrate hearts, but are quite different from the state of affairs in any other invertebrates. In most arthropods and annelids, for instance, the hearts are neurogenic and the principal accelerator is acetylcholine. Gnathobdellid leeches are clearly exceptional in this respect, and this is further evidence that their circulatory system is not homologous with the blood system of other annelids. The source of the adrenalin in leeches appears to be the ganglia of the ventral nerve cord, for Gaskell (1919) demonstrated the chromaffin staining reaction in certain cells of the ventral ganglia and identified adrenalin in ganglion extract. Perez (1942) confirmed this result although he thought that the adrenalin was more localized in its distribution than Gaskell had suggested.

Leeches are predominantly freshwater animals, but many freshwater habitats contain water which is only partially air-saturated. There have been several investigations into the rate of oxygen uptake by leeches at various oxygen concentrations of the water. Early experiments with *Hirudo* (Lindeman, 1932, 1935) involved placing the leeches in water in a closed container. Samples of water were drawn off at intervals and from the rate of fall of oxygen concentration the oxygen uptake of the leeches was calculated. It appeared that *Hirudo* was able to maintain a constant rate of oxygen uptake independent of the oxygen concentration down to about 10–20% air-saturation, the precise level depending on the temperature. Similar experiments by Hiestand and Singer (1934) and by Sgonina (quoted by Herter, 1936) gave rather different results. These discrepancies were probably due to variation in the state of nutrition, time of year and degree of acclimatization.

In more recent work (Mann, 1956) these variables have been eliminated as far as possible. In Fig. 29 is shown the oxygen consumption of five species of leech at various oxygen concentrations. In these experiments the leeches were placed in a small container with water of a known oxygen concentration and left for about 1 hr, during which time the oxygen concentration fell by a relatively small amount. From the final oxygen concentration it was possible to determine the oxygen consumption at the mean concentration of the experiment. To build up the curves shown in Fig. 29 large numbers of such experiments were carried out, each point on the graph being the mean of at least five determinations. The highest rate of oxygen uptake in air-saturated water is shown by *Piscicola geometra*, the piscicolid fish parasite. This leech has to be very active indeed when it is seeking a host and is provided with

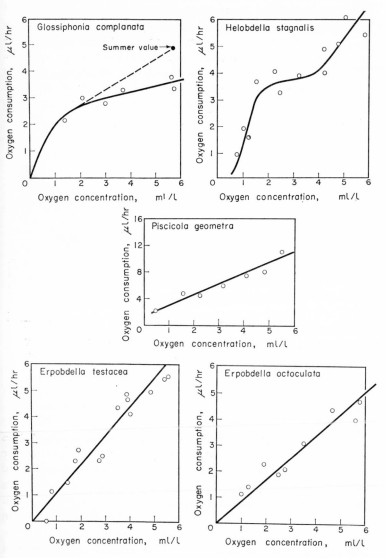

FIG. 29.   Oxygen consumption of various species of leech at 20°C at various oxygen concentrations. From Mann, 1956.

pulsatile vesicles so it is perhaps not surprising that its rate of
metabolism is high. In the two *Erpobdella* species as well as in
Piscicola the oxygen uptake was proportional to the oxygen
concentration of the water, suggesting that low oxygen concentrations produced no special physiological response from the animals.
The curves for *Glossiphonia complanata* and *Helobdella stagnalis*
on the other hand are comparatively level over part of the range
of oxygen concentration, suggesting that there is some regulation
of oxygen uptake by the leeches.

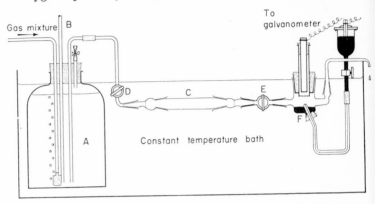

FIG. 29a. Apparatus used in leech respiration studies, giving
the results illustrated in Fig. 32. The leeches were placed in
the chamber C and subjected to a constant stream of water
from reservoir A, driven by pressure from a gas or air cylinder.
The oxygen content of the outflow was determined by a drop-
ping mercury electrode in chamber F. From Mann, 1958.

The experiments described above were all repeated with leeches
which were allowed to become acclimatized overnight to the
oxygen concentration of the experiment. Only one leech responded
to this treatment, *Erpobdella testacea*, which began to regulate its
oxygen uptake at concentrations above $\frac{1}{3}$ air-saturation (Fig. 30).
Further investigations showed that such acclimatization occurs in
summer but not in winter. This leech lives in ponds which are
relatively anaerobic in summer and the adaptive significance of
such a mechanism is clear. When the actual method of adaptation
was studied it was established that the leech did not make ventilatory movements so presumably it increased its rate of circulation.

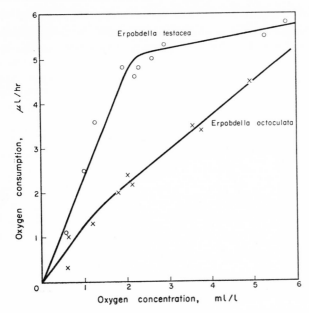

Fig. 30. The relation between oxygen consumption and oxygen concentration in the two species of *Erpobdella* after acclimatization overnight to the concentration of oxygen at which the readings were taken. From Mann, 1956.

The low oxygen concentrations must have stimulated the adrenergic mechanism, thus accelerating the rate of contraction of the lateral sinuses.

It is of interest to enquire into the function of haemoglobin in leeches, for in many annelids such as *Arenicola* it is of value only under conditions of extremely low oxygen concentrations in the surrounding water. In *Lumbricus* it seems likely that the haemoglobin transports between one-quarter and one-half of the oxygen used by the worms. Johnson (1942) compared the oxygen consumption of *Lumbricus herculeus* at various concentrations of atmospheric oxygen, before and after the inactivation of the haemoglobin with carbon monoxide, care being taken to ensure that the respiratory enzymes were not affected. She concluded that the haemoglobin of the blood was responsible for carrying about 23% of the respired oxygen when the oxygen pressure was

152 mm, 35% at 76 mm and 40% at 38 mm (Fig. 31). When similar experiments were carried out with the leech *Erpobdella testacea* it was found that after carbon monoxide treatment the oxygen consumption fell by 45% in air-saturated water and by 25% in ⅓ air-saturated water (Mann, 1958). This suggests

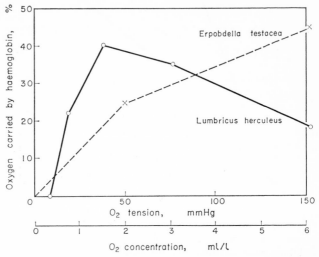

FIG. 31. The percentage of oxygen carried by the haemoglobin of an earthworm and a leech at various oxygen tensions. From data in Johnson, 1942 and Mann, 1958.

that in *Erpobdella* as in *Lumbricus*, the haemoglobin functions in oxygen transport at all normal oxygen concentrations of the environment. Haemoglobin appears to play no essential part in acclimatization to low oxygen concentrations, as it does in the Cladocera for instance, for *E. testacea* was able to acclimatize even after the haemoglobin had been inactivated (Fig. 32). Many leeches have a considerable ability to withstand anaerobic conditions. Numerous examples are quoted by von Brand (1946). *Hirudo medicinalis, Haemopis sanguisuga, Helobdella stagnalis* and *Erpobdella octoculata* survived for about 5 days at room temperature while *Glossiphonia complanata* was able to survive for 16 days at 14–16°C without oxygen. Pütter showed that *Hirudo* survived only 3–5 days if it had been recently fed but over 10 days when starving. This may well have been because the oxygen requirements of the recently fed leeches were higher. Hyman (1929) showed that the oxygen uptake of planarians was high shortly after feeding. The oxygen consumption of the leech *Erpobdella testacea* rose fourfold soon after feeding (Mann, 1958). Von Brand (1946) has reviewed the evidence for the occurrence

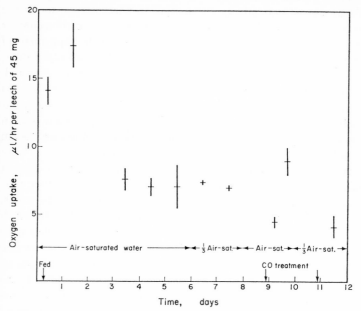

FIG. 32.   Mean oxygen consumption of twenty-two *Erpobdella testacea* of average weight 45 mg, subjected to various treatments as indicated. Lines are drawn to represent twice the standard error above and below each point. After feeding the rate of oxygen uptake rose to a high level, but settled to about 7 μl/h/leech on the fourth to sixth days. On transfer to water of low oxygen content this rate of oxygen uptake was maintained but after treatment with carbon monoxide the leeches failed to maintain a normal rate of respiration in water of low oxygen content. From Mann, 1958.

of anaerobiosis in invertebrates and pointed out that when the concentration of the oxygen in the environment falls many animals have an increased consumption of carbohydrate, a greater production of organic acids and a higher respiratory quotient, indicating that anaerobic fermentation is taking place. He has further suggested that the critical oxygen tension below which the oxygen uptake of an animal falls rapidly is the tension at which the metabolism changes from a mainly aerobic to a mainly anaerobic type.

There is clear evidence from the work of Braconnier-Fayemendy (1933) that *Hirudo* effects a transition to anaerobiosis, for in the absence of oxygen there is a fourfold increase in the carbon content of the urine. Moreover, there is no evidence of the repayment of an oxygen debt after anaerobic metabolism (Hiestand and Singer, 1934) so the products of anaerobiosis must have been excreted. In the other leeches whose oxygen uptake in relation to oxygen tension has been studied it is probable that all are able to carry out anaerobic metabolism, but those best adapted to life in low oxygen concentrations are those which can maintain aerobic metabolism to the lowest level of oxygen in the environment.

When leeches find themselves in water of low oxygen content they tend to move to the surface. In extreme conditions they protrude the anterior half of the body from the surface of the water, thus in effect carrying out aerial respiration. During the nineteenth century medicinal leeches were kept in jars and if the leeches were restless or rose to the surface this was taken as a forecast of bad weather. The explanation of this phenomenon is not clear, presumably they responded to falling barometric pressure. It has recently been shown that earthworms and many other organisms show a correlation between respiratory rate and barometric pressure (Brown, 1957) so the leeches may have responded directly to pressure changes, but a fall in atmospheric pressure will also lead to a small fall in the concentration of dissolved oxygen in the water, so it is also possible that the leeches responded to this, and only indirectly to the pressure changes.

CHAPTER 7

MUSCLE, NERVE AND LOCOMOTION

1. The Muscular System

LOCOMOTION in annelids in general is brought about by the antagonistic action of two sets of muscles, the longitudinal muscles whose fibres lie parallel to the longitudinal axis of the body and the circular muscles whose fibres lie in a plane at right angles to the longitudinal axis. The forces produced by one set of muscles are used to stretch the others through the hydraulic action of the fluid enclosed within the body wall. Thus an annelid may be compared with a fluid filled cylinder which, when the circular muscles contract, becomes long and thin and when the longitudinal muscles contract becomes short and thick. In earthworms there are internal septa which limit the movement of coelomic fluid and help one part of the body to be longitudinally contracted while another part is longitudinally extended, but in many polychaetes the septa are reduced or absent so that several segments work as a unit. In leeches the whole body works as a unit and all septa have disappeared. Moreover the coelomic fluid has been replaced by mesenchyme cells but these are sufficiently deformable to provide the hydraulic mechansim described above.

Between the outer circular muscles and the inner longitudinals leeches have a double layer of oblique muscles whose fibres run at approximately 45° to right and left of the longitudinal axis (Fig. 33). This condition is unique among annelids. In most species they run spirally round the body in complete right and left geodesic helices. The mode of action of these muscles has not been investigated experimentally but Clark and Cowey (1958) have considered the geometry of a geodesic system of inextensible fibres in some nemertean worms and turbellarians and this gives

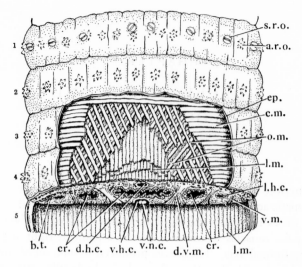

FIG. 33. Diagram of muscles of body wall of *Hirudinaria*.
Note oblique muscles. *a.r.o*, annular receptor organ; *b.t*,
botryoidal tissue; *c.m*, circular muscles; *cr*, crop; *d.h.c*, dorsal
haemocoelomic channel; *d.v.m.* dorso-ventral muscles; *ep*,
epidermis; *l.h.c*, lateral haemocoelomic channel; *l.m*, longitudinal muscles; *o.m*, oblique muscles; *s.r.o*, segmental receptor
organs; *v.h.c*, ventral haemocoelomic channel; *v.m*, vertical
muscles; *v.n.c*, ventral nerve cord; 1–5, serial numbers of annuli.
From Bhatia, 1941.

us some idea of what is likely to happen with fibres that are
contractile.

Considering the nemertean as a fluid-filled cylinder in whose
walls runs a system of inextensible spiral fibres, we see that the
shape of the cylinder can be altered by changing the angle θ which
the fibres make with the longitudinal axis (Fig. 34). The volume
contained by such a cylinder is maximal when the angle θ is 54° 44′.
If the volume of the contained fluid were equal to the maximum
volume of the system there would be no possibility of changing
shape, so the volume of the fluid is something less than maximal
and the difference is taken up when necessary by the animal
becoming elliptical in cross section. In leeches the geometry is
comparable but the fibres are contractile. When the fibres are at
54° 44′ to the longitudinal axis this is the position at which they

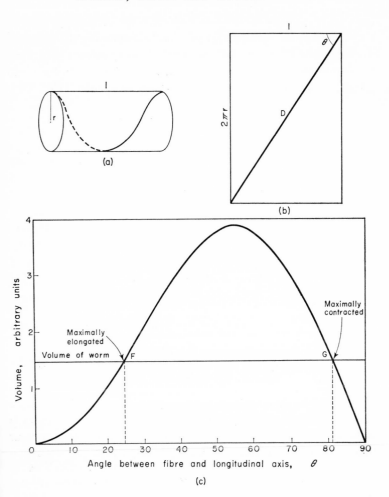

Fɪɢ. 34. The relation between the volume of a cylindrical system bounded by inextensible fibres of length D and the angle θ which the fibres make with longitudinal axis. (a) the course of a single fibre; (b) the cylinder slit lengthwise and opened out; (c) the relation between angle θ and volume of the system, which is maximal when $\theta = 54°\,44'$ The horizontal line represents the volume of an animal which is less than the maximum permitted by the fibres. The limits of θ are at F and G. From Clark and Cowey, 1958.

contract maximally for a given body volume. When the body is long and thin the spiral fibres are clearly reinforcing the action of the longitudinal muscles and causing the body to shorten (Fig. 35a). When the leech is short and thick the spiral fibres reinforce the action of the circular muscles and cause elongation (Fig. 35b).

(a)

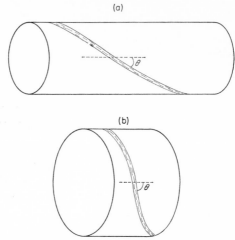

(b)

FIG. 35.   Diagram illustrating how spiral muscles may reinforce the action of (a) the longitudinal muscles or (b) the circular muscles. For explanation, see text.

There must be some intermediate position when the spiral muscles cause neither lengthening nor shortening, and this is when they make an angle of 54° 44′ with the longitudinal axis. At this point they serve only to increase internal hydrostatic pressure, imparting rigidity to the body of the leech. This enables the leech to sit upright on its posterior sucker, an activity which is characteristic of certain leeches and important in their behaviour.

Leeches also have a well developed set of dorso–ventral muscles. These, on contraction, make the body flat and ribbon-like, thus increasing the efficiency of the dorso–ventral undulations used in swimming.

The longitudinal, circular and dorso–ventral muscle cells of leeches are elongated unstriated cells with an inner axial sarcoplasm and an outer rind of contractile myoplasm. In the longitudinal and circular muscles they are usually simple spindle-shaped structures but in the dorso–ventral muscles they are frequently branched at the ends, providing multiple insertions into the body wall. The nucleus is usually in the central sarcoplasm but in a few cases it is in a lateral protuberance of the sarcoplasm (Fig. 36c). The myoplasm consists of large numbers of myofibrillae regularly arranged and separated one from the other by thin lamellae of sarcoplasm (Fig. 36a). In *Haemopis* longitudinal muscle cells are

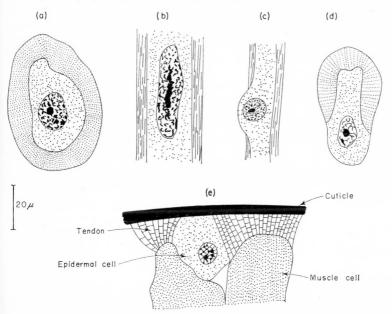

(a)   (b)   (c)   (d)

20μ

(e)   Cuticle

Tendon

Epidermal cell

Muscle cell

FIG. 36.   (a) and (b) transverse and longitudinal sections of part of a normal muscle fibre; (c) and (d) sections showing how the sarcoplasm may form a lateral protuberance; (e) the attachment of a muscle to the cuticle, after Sukatschoff, 1912.

5–15 mm long when moderately contracted (Schwab, 1949). In a nerve–muscle preparation contraction may be initiated by electrical stimulation of the nerve or muscle or by immersion in a dilute solution of acetylcholine. The latter reaction has been used as a test for the presence of acetylcholine (Minz, 1932) as contractions are produced with concentrations as low as 1×10^{-9}. Eserine increases the response to a given stimulus, but curare inhibits it. It has recently been found that morphine in the appropriate concentration facilitates relaxation without affecting the sensitivity to acetylcholine, so that the best method of preparing leech muscle for assay of acetylcholine is to treat it with morphine and eserine sulphate (Murnaghan, 1958). During electrical stimulation acetylcholine is released into the surrounding fluid and it therefore seems likely that it has been produced at the neuromuscular junction, and that this is the normal mechanism for inducing contraction (Bacq and Coppée, 1937). Cholinesterase is present in both the muscles and the ventral nerve cord and presumably hydrolyses the acetylcholine as soon as it has done its work. Eserine inhibits cholinesterase, so this accounts for its effect of increasing the response to stimulation.

The rate of action of leech longitudinal muscle is slow, considering that it is concerned with locomotion, escape reactions and attachment to host. Schwab (1949) studied the time constants of dorsal longitudinal muscle of *Haemopis*. Table 2 shows that it is

TABLE 2. TIME CONSTANTS OF VARIOUS MUSCLES

	Contraction time (msec)	Relaxation time	Chronaxie (msec)	Conduction rate
Haemopis				
dorsal long	500	27 sec	68	49 cm/sec
Frog				
sartorius	40	55 msec	3	2·4 m/sec
gastrocnemius	150	—	0·3	—
Crayfish				
claw (fast)	200	1 sec	1·2	20 cm/sec
Helix				
foot	200	"several" sec	20	—
Pecten				
slow adductor	500	45 sec	—	—
Cat diaphragm	480	—	5–6	35 cm/sec

much slower than vertebrate limb muscle, e.g. frog sartorius, and is more nearly comparable with such muscles as *Pecten* slow adductor or cat diaphragm. Similar results were obtained with the muscle of *Hirudo* by Lapicque and Veil (1925) who compared them with the muscles of the body wall of an earthworm. They found that the chronaxies were 30 msec for *Hirudo* and 20 msec for earthworm, while conduction rates were about 35 cm/sec.

The response of leech muscle to electrical stimulation is decreased by immersion in hypotonic solutions of sodium chloride or sugar (Winterstein and Ozer, 1949), but the same treatment increases the amount of tonic contraction, suggesting that the mechanism of contraction after stimulation is quite distinct from the mechanism for maintaining tonus. Moreover, while increased activity under electrical stimulation is associated with increased oxygen consumption, there is no such relation between tonus and oxygen consumption (Ozer and Winterstein, 1949). The oxygen consumption is maximal when the muscle is immersed in $0 \cdot 1$ N sodium chloride and at other concentrations the oxygen consumption is lower irrespective of whether the tonus is increased or decreased.

2. THE NERVOUS SYSTEM

The gross morphology of the central nervous system of *Hirudo* has been described and the differences in other genera are mainly ones of relative proportions. In this section we shall consider the micro-anatomy of the nervous system of a typical segment in order to provide a background for the understanding of its physiology. As in most annelids the motor nerve cells are concentrated in the ventral nerve cord while the sensory nerve cells lie peripherally, in or near the sense organs. In earthworms the nerve cells are widely distributed in the ventral half of the ventral cord with special concentrations in the segmental ganglia, but in leeches the motor cell bodies are found almost entirely in the ganglia, enclosed within fibrous capsules so that they are sharply separated from the mass of fibres which form the bulk of the nerve cord. There are, however, certain cells in the fibrous mass. They are spindle shaped when viewed from the side and star shaped in cross section. Miller (1945) regards them as nerve cells but most authors, notably Scriban and Autrum (1934) and Ito (1936) consider that they are neuroglia, i.e. supporting cells whose processes bind together the nerve fibres.

Each ganglion has six cell capsules, two antero–dorsal in position, two postero–dorsal and two median ventrals. A typical transverse section (Fig. 37) passes through two dorsal and one ventral capsule and shows the nerve cells as pear-shaped structures with their narrow ends directed towards the centre of the ganglion. They

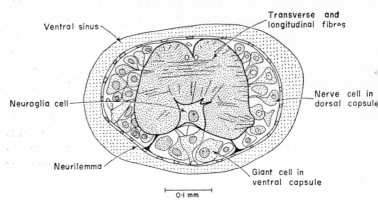

Fig. 37. Transverse section through a ventral ganglion of *Haemopis*.

give off processes which pass through the capsule wall and join the fibrous mass. The course of the axons was studied by Retzius (1891) and by Havet (1900) and their work has not been improved upon. The main motor axons run from a given cell capsule into the lateral segmental nerves of their own or the opposite side of the body. Internuncial neurones form synaptic connexions with both sensory and motor fibres, often running from one ganglion to the next along the ventral cord. In addition to these there is a giant cell in each ventral capsule and this has an axon which forks, sending one process into the ventral cord and two into lateral segmental nerves. There are no giant fibres of the type seen in earthworms and polychaetes, but from the behaviour of leeches it is clear that there is a fast conducting system (Miller, 1942). From Retzius' figures the axons of the "giant nerve cells" appear to be about twice the diameter of a normal nerve fibre. It is doubtful whether these fibres would mediate the startle reaction of leeches unless they were also myelinated. Wilson (1960) studied the effect of stimulating an isolated segmental nerve of *Hirudo* and found no evidence of a quick response in the peripheral neuromuscular system. Horridge and Roberts (1960) reached the

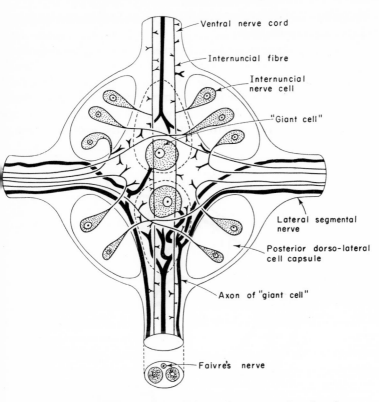

Ventral nerve cord

Internuncial fibre

Internuncial nerve cell

"Giant cell"

Lateral segmental nerve

Posterior dorso-lateral cell capsule

Axon of "giant cell"

Faivre's nerve

FIG. 38. Diagram illustrating the main routes taken by the processes of the nerve cells lying in the ventral ganglion of a leech. The four dorsal capsules are shown in firm outline, the two median ventral ones in dotted outline. After Scriban, 1934, based on the work of Retzius and Havet.

same conclusion regarding the segmental nerves of earthworms. This is an interesting difference between annelids and arthropods, for in the latter there is multiple innervation of muscle fibres, providing for both quick and slow response. The ventral nerve cord of leeches contains a large number of fibres mostly extending over no more than one segment; it is perhaps not surprising that the normal conduction rate in this cord is rather low, of the order of 18 cm/sec in *Haemopis* according to Schwab (1949), and 40 cm/sec in *Hirudo* according to Lapicque and Veil (1925). Schwab found substantial quantities of both acetylcholine and cholinesterase in the ventral nerve cord of *Haemopis*.

The general pattern of lateral nerves is that from each segmental ganglion arise two pairs of nerves. The anterior ones run ventrally at first and then turn outwards following the curvature of the body wall while the posterior pair run to the dorsal half of the body serving primarily the dorsal body wall, but also sending a branch to the organs in the postero–ventral part of the segment. Each of

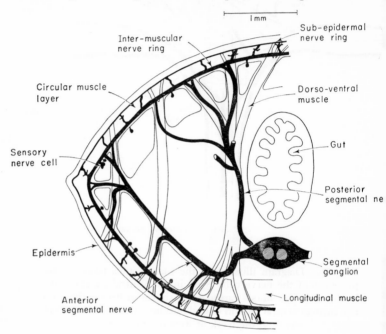

FIG. 39. Diagram illustrating the lateral segmental nerves and peripheral nerves of *Erpobdella*. After Bristol, 1898.

these lateral segmental nerves connects with an inter-muscular nerve ring which circles the body between circular and longitudinal muscles. There are two of these in each segment, corresponding in position with the anterior and posterior pairs of lateral nerves. There are nerve fibres running longitudinally between the intermuscular rings and others which run to the nervous system lying immediately below the epidermis. Bristol (1898) described

ub-epidermal nerve rings corresponding in number and position
vith the inter-muscular rings, and it has been suggested (Miller,
945) that there is also a network of nerve fibres just below the
pidermis comparable with that described for the earthworm by
Iess (1925). On the other hand Wilson (1960) studied the spread
of excitation over the body wall of *Hirudo* after stimulation of an
solated segmental nerve and concluded that no nerve net was
present. Iwata (1940a, b) reached a similar conclusion regarding
. Japanese leech. The sense organs of the epidermis and the
proprioceptor organs in the body wall send neurones into the
peripheral network of fibres and from here they pass down the
egmental nerves to the ventral nerve cord.

3. LOCOMOTION

Having discussed the structure and function of the nervous
and muscular systems we may now pass to the co-ordinated
activity of these systems as seen in locomotion. Broadly speaking,
eeches move in two ways: by swimming, which involves dorso–
ventral undulations of the body and by creeping, which involves
noving the anterior sucker forward and drawing the posterior one
up behind. Gray *et al.* (1938) resolved these activities into a
system of reflex responses. Stated rather simply, the sequence is
is follows: if *Hirudo* is freely suspended in water so that neither
he suckers nor the ventral body surface are able to make contact
with a solid object it will swim, the dorso–ventral muscles being
contracted and the circular muscles relaxed while dorso–ventral
undulations pass back along the body as a result of differential
contraction of the longitudinal muscles. If the anterior sucker is
now brought into contact with a solid object it attaches firmly and
the swimming stops; the dorso–ventral and circular muscles relax
and the longitudinals contract, causing the body to become short
and thick. If now the posterior sucker is placed in contact with a
solid object it becomes attached and a wave of contraction passes
back over the circular muscles while the longitudinals are inhibited,
causing the body to become long and thin. Repetition of the last
two reflex actions results in crawling. Gray *et al.* therefore concluded that if ventral peripheral stimulation is absent the leech
swims, if it is present it crawls; and that the rhythm of crawling is

determined by a recurrent pattern of stimulation via the ventral
suckers. It should perhaps be added at this point that crawling is
not produced entirely by elongating and shortening the body.
In most species, when the posterior sucker is drawn forward the
body is flexed in a dorso–ventral plane, enabling the posterior
sucker to be placed immediately behind the anterior one (Fig. 40).

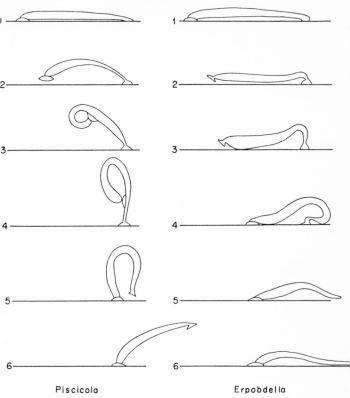

Piscicola   Erpobdella

FIG. 40. Successive stages in the creeping of *Piscicola* and
Erpobdella. After Herter, 1929, modified.

Chapman (1958) has pointed out that contraction of the dorso–
ventral muscles in the middle region of the body assists this
flexure. The movement is more marked in some species than in
others and in its extreme form is reminiscent of the movement of
a looper caterpillar.

4. Co-ordination

Various experiments have been conducted on *Hirudo* and *Haemopis* to elucidate the role of the nervous system in locomotion. Rhythmical electrical activity is found in the ventral nerve cord of a swimming leech, but this becomes irregular if the nerve cord is isolated from peripheral stimulation by cutting all segmental nerves. If the cord is isolated from the supra- and sub-oesophageal ganglia by transection just behind the head the electrical activity disappears. If the body of a leech is cut transversely leaving only the ventral nerve cord intact the two halves will show co-ordinated locomotory activity (Fig. 41), but if the nerve cord only is tran-

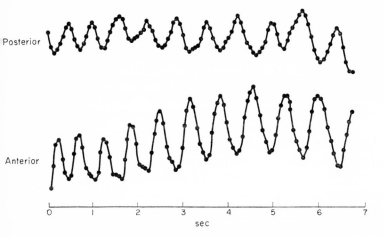

FIG. 41. Record, taken from a cinematograph film, showing co-ordinated swimming movements of the anterior and posterior regions of a leech which were connected by nerve cord only. From Gray *et al.*, 1938.

sected the activity on either side of the cut is unco-ordinated. Anterior to the cut the body becomes rounded in cross section as for crawling, and there is an increase in tonus in the circular muscles. Posterior to the cut the body becomes flattened and may perform swimming movements, while there is a loss of tonus in the circular muscles. It thus appears that the ventral nerve cord plays a vital role in the co-ordination of locomotion but it only does so when stimulated from the peripheral nervous system or the ganglionic masses.

Clearly the reflex pattern described by Gray *et al.* is only part of the mechanism of locomotion, for there are many exceptions to the pattern they described. When a leech changes from crawling to swimming it does so in spite of the ventral peripheral stimulation which it is receiving. When it performs ventilatory movements it in effect swims while retaining a hold with the ventral sucker (Fig. 42). It is likely that the large ganglionic masses of the head

FIG. 42.   Lateral view of *Erpobdella* with ventilatory movements in progress.

and anal regions play a part in determining locomotory behaviour. Kaiser (1954) has considered in some detail the experimental evidence for ganglionic activity. Decapitated leeches swim more readily and for longer periods than intact ones. This is partly due, no doubt, to the fact that the ventral nerve cord no longer receives impulses from the anterior sucker, as these would normally initiate crawling. The swimming movements of a suspended leech may be stopped by stroking the ventral surface and conversely they may be accentuated by gentle dorsal stimulation. However, if the cerebral ganglion is removed while the suboesophaegeal is left intact the leech is still abnormally active. It appears that one of the functions of the cerebral ganglion is to inhibit locomotion under certain circumstances. Another function, which we may deduce from a study of the pathways of nerve fibres, is to receive and sift information from the sense organs of the head.

Removal of the sub-oesophageal ganglion brings about a number of changes at one time. It isolates the ventral nerve cord from the influence of the brain, isolates it from peripheral stimulation through the anterior sucker and removes the influence of the sub-oesophageal ganglion. Leeches treated thus appear to be almost incapable of crawling, remaining inert for long periods. Buddenbrock (1953) has pointed out that a number of experimental results are explained by supposing that in response to peripheral stimulation the sub-oesophageal ganglion excites the ventral nerve cord to co-ordinate crawling activity. There are four situations in which it might fail to do so: (i) when there is no ventral peripheral stimulation, (ii) when inhibited by the brain, (iii) when the ganglion has been removed and (iv) when the nerve cord has been cut. Taken together these account for all the experimental and behavioural observations quoted above.

According to Schluter (1933) removal of the anal ganglion inhibits swimming so that leeches dropped into water fall passively to the bottom. Removal of the brain of such leeches restores the powers of swimming. It is thus possible that the division of labour between the various ganglionic masses is as follows: the sub-oesophageal ganglion is mainly responsible for initiating and maintaining crawling movements, the anal ganglion for swimming movements and the supra-oesophageal ganglion for inhibiting locomotion under certain circumstances.

It is interesting and instructive to compare the locomotion of leeches with that of earthworms. In the latter, the basic mechanism is that a group of segments becomes elongated, obtains a point of attachment anteriorly by protrusion of chaetae and then shortens, drawing the posterior segments forward. Chaetae are then protruded on the posterior segments before the next phase of elongation begins. Normally, several waves of activity are present in the body at one time, but the author has observed that in certain circumstances one wave of activity may occupy almost the whole body at least in certain species of earthworm. From this condition it is only a short step to the arrangement found in leeches. The anterior and posterior suckers replace the chaetae as means of attachment and in crawling the whole body is involved in one wave of activity.

It is no longer necessary for the body to be divided internally into a number of distinct hydraulic units capable of independent activity and this is probably the functional reason for the loss of septa and the obliteration of the spacious coelom in leeches. Earthworms are capable of co-ordinated movement after nerve cord transection and even after the body has been completely severed and joined again by stitches. Apparently a peripheral mechanism for the transmission of locomotor reflexes is present in earthworms but not in leeches. Ventral stimulation by contact with the substratum is necessary for normal locomotion in both earthworms and leeches. The ventral nerve cord is capable of co-ordinating crawling without the assistance of the head ganglia but does not normally do so in the absence of peripheral stimulation. Swimming by leeches is an activity for which there is no parallel in earthworms, and the anal ganglion appears to be necessary for normal swimming. Although locomotion in both forms can be reduced to a pattern of reflexes there is no doubt that the brain exerts a modifying influence on the pattern in response to the stimulation of external conditions or internal physiological needs.

CHAPTER 8

SENSE ORGANS AND
BEHAVIOUR

1. SENSORY EQUIPMENT

THE basic sensory equipment of leeches corresponds almost exactly with that of earthworms, but the sensory elements are grouped into slightly more complex organs and the nervous system appears to be capable of co-ordinating rather more complex patterns of behaviour. This is not surprising when we remember that many leeches rely for their nourishment on their ability to make contact with vertebrate hosts capable of rapid movement.

There are three kinds of sensory equipment: free ending nerve fibres in the epidermis, epidermal sense cells and light sensitive cells. The free ending nerve fibres (Fig. 43a) are the terminations of nerves arising either from the main segmental nerves or, more often, from the sub-epidermal or inter-muscular nerve rings described on p. 72. It is probable that they respond to changes in temperature or to mechanical stimuli resulting from deformation of the epidermis through contact with solid objects. The epidermal sense cells (Fig. 43b) are tall spindle shaped cells occurring singly or in groups among the other epidermal cells. Their outer ends terminate in fine sensory hairs which pass through the cuticle and project about 10μ beyond it, while their inner ends lead to sensory nerve fibres. Groups of such cells are called sensillae and are scattered over various parts of the body, being particularly numerous on the head. In most leeches there are also sensillae which are regularly arranged on the middle annulus of each segment and are known as segmental receptors. In the different species the segmental receptors attain varying degrees of complexity and may include light sensitive cells, mucous glands and special muscle cells which enable them to be protruded as papillae or retracted as cup

79

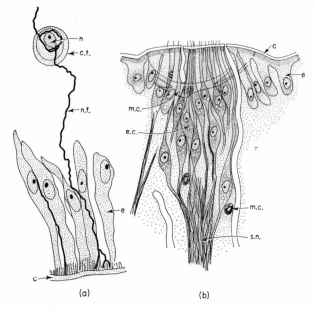

FIG. 43. (a) A free-ending nerve fibre in the epidermis of
Hirudo medicinalis.
(b) Epidermal sense cells grouped in a sensilla.
b.m, basement membrane; *c,* cuticle; *c.t,* connective tissue
sheath surrounding a nerve cell; *e,* epidermal cell; *e.c.,* epidermal
sense cell; *n,* nucleus of nerve cell; *n.f,* nerve fibre; *m.c,* muscle
cell; *s.n,* sensory nerve.
From Grassé, 1959, based on Apathy (a) and Autrum (b).

shaped organs. The functions of the sensillae are presumably
either tactile or chemoreceptive but it has not been possible to
distinguish one from the other in a particular organ. There is
some evidence that the chemoreceptors are confined to the head
region (Kaiser, 1954) and if this is so, the sensillae of the general
body surface are touch receptors.

Light sensitive cells (Fig. 44) are recognizable by the large
vacuole filled with hyaline, possibly albuminous fluid which acts
as a lens. Light is concentrated on to a neurofibrillar network
within the cytoplasm which makes contact with a sensory nerve
fibre. Such cells occur in small numbers in the sensillae or sometimes in the general epidermis but leeches, unlike earthworms,

have distinct eyes formed from a number of light sensitive cells backed by a pigmented cup. In some leeches, such as *Piscicola*, the eyes are quite simple structures consisting of a small number of photoreceptors in a shallow cup, but we may construct a series

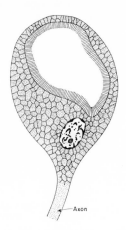

Axon

FIG. 44.   Light sensitive cell from *Erpobdella octoculata*. From Grassé, 1959, based on Autrum.

showing a progressive increase in the number of photoreceptors involved and in the depth of the pigmented cup until we reach the condition described in *Hirudo* (p. 19) where there are very many photoreceptors enclosed in a deep and narrow pigmented cup. Such an eye has better directional properties than the simpler kinds. It is also more superficial than the eyes of the glossiphoniids so that it is less affected by the light scattering properties of the tissues above it. Another improvement is in the disposition of the nerve fibres. In *Piscicola* the fibres leaving the photoreceptors pass out over the rim of the pigmented cup, thus interfering with the passage of light to some extent. In *Erpobdella* the nerve fibres may pass through the side of the pigmented cup and in *Hirudo* they pass down the centre of the eye and out at the base of the pigment cup, thus affording the minimum interference with incident light. In its most advanced form a leech eye should be capable of giving a highly directional response to light rays and when, as in *Hirudo*, there are several eyes pointing in various directions it should be possible to obtain a crude impression of form and movement. Boehm (1947) identified a red fluorescent porphyrin in the pigment layer of the eyes of *Hirudo*. It is known that the presence of certain porphyrins renders protoplasm light sensitive but as this substance is in the pigment cup its physiological function is not understood.

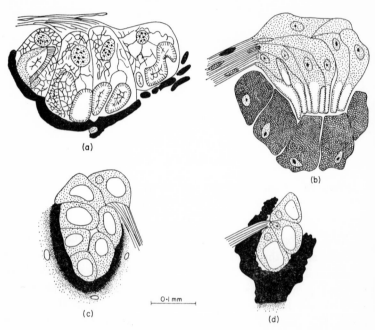

FIG. 45. Various leech eyes in vertical section. (a) *Piscicola geometra;* (b) *Glossiphonia complanata;* (c) and (d) *Erpobdella.* (a) after Maier 1892, (b), (c) and (d) after Hesse, 1897.

Apart from behaviour associated with reproduction, which is complex and difficult to observe, the normal behaviour of leeches seems to be relatively simple and amenable to detailed analysis. Broadly speaking the animals are either in a state of hunger and respond to any stimulus which might indicate the presence of a suitable food organism or they have food in the crop and rest in a position where they are reasonably safe from predators. In the latter condition they appear to avoid light, to seek the contact stimulus afforded by creeping under a stone or into a leaf axil and to be relatively insensitive to chemical or vibration stimuli. In the hungry condition they may come out into the light, change their colour and be roused to activity by vibrations in the water, by scents emanating from a food organism or by a passing shadow. The foundations of our knowledge of leech behaviour were laid by the careful descriptive work of Gee (1912) who studied the American erpobdellid *Dina microstoma* and the glossiphoniid *Helobdella stagnalis*. The study was carried much further by Herter in a series of papers published between 1928 and 1942 on the behaviour of certain German freshwater leeches. These papers are listed in the bibliography and will not be mentioned individually in the account which follows.

2. REACTIONS TO LIGHT

In general leeches are strongly photonegative in their behaviour, some species more so than others. Table 3 shows the result of a series of observations in which leeches were given the choice of a lighted or a shaded part of an aquarium. On each of 20 days the position of each leech was noted and the shading was moved to the opposite side. In the experiments where only one leech was present in each experimental tank (columns 1 and 2) the majority of leeches chose the shade every time. Those that did not were *Hirudo* the medicinal leech, *Theromyzon* the duck leech, and *Hemiclepsis* a parasite of fish and amphibia. Hungry *Theromyzon* were much more frequently photopositive than satiated specimens, suggesting that in these blood-sucking species it is the need to obtain a meal which modifies their normal light avoiding reactions. Where there were several leeches in each experiment the percentage of leeches taking up positions in the lighted zone was considerably increased (columns 3–5).

Herter and later Denzer-Melbrandt (1935) gave leeches a choice of four intensities of illumination which may be referred to as lighted, lightly shaded, heavily shaded and dark. The percentage

TABLE 3. THE DISTRIBUTION OF LEECHES BETWEEN LIGHTED AND SHADED PARTS OF AN AQUARIUM

Species	Single leech		Several leeches		
	1 In light (%)	2 In shade (%)	3 Number of leeches	4 In light (%)	5 In shade (%)
Piscicola geometra	0	100	6	2·9	97·1
Hemiclepsis marginata	35	65	3	25·9	74·1
Theromyzon tessulatum (gut full)	11·8	88·2	3 } gut fairly full	33·3	66·7
Theromyzon tessulatum (hungry)	80·0	20			
Glossiphonia complanata	0	100	5	21·2	78·8
Glossiphonia heteroclita	0	100	8	27·2	72·8
Helobdella stagnalis	0	100	6	4·5	95·5
Hirudo medicinalis	35	65	—	—	—
Erpobdella sp.	0	100	3	15·4	84·6

of times that each leech settled in each zone is recorded graphically in Fig. 46. This shows *Glossiphonia heteroclita* as the most strongly photonegative in its behaviour. It also shows that blood-sucking parasites of vertebrates settled more often in the lighted zone than in either of the partially shaded ones. Apparently when these

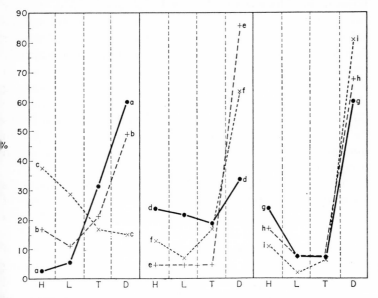

FIG. 46.   The distribution of various species of leech between (H) lighted, (L) lightly shaded, (T) heavily shaded and (D) dark zones of an aquarium in a large number of trials.   *a, Piscicola geometra; b, Hemiclepsis marginata; c, Theromyzon tessulatum; d, Glossiphonia complanata; e, G. heteroclita; f, Helobdella stagnalis; g, Hirudo medicinalis; h, Haemopis sanguisuga; i, Erpobdella.* From Herter, 1936.

species are seeking a host they are photopositive, not merely indifferent to light. By contrast, the two species of *Glossiphonia* were found in lighted or partially shaded zones with about equal frequency.

Up to this point we have been concerned only with reactions to diffuse lighting from above. Various people have also studied the reactions of leeches to a beam of light from a single source. Holmes (1905) gave a clear description of the behaviour of

Glossiphonia in such a situation. "In its progress the leech frequently raises the extended anterior part of the body and waves it from side to side as if feeling its way. If the animal turns it in the direction of a strong light it is quickly withdrawn and extended again, usually in another direction. If the light is less strong it waves its head back and forth several times and sets it down away from the light; then the caudal end is brought forward and the anterior end extended and swayed about and set down still further from the light than before. When the leech becomes negatively oriented it may crawl away from the light, like the earthworm, in a nearly straight line. The extension, withdrawal and swaying about of the anterior end of the body enable the animal to locate the direction of least stimulation and when that is found it begins its regular movements of locomotion. Of a number of random movements in all directions only those are followed up which bring the animal out of the undesirable situation."

The swaying of the anterior end of the leech, which Herter calls *Suchbewegung*, searching movement, is very characteristic of leeches which are crawling, or are about to do so. Gee said "This tendency to 'prove all things, hold fast to that which is good' is perhaps the most striking single characteristic of the behaviour of leeches . . .". Herter showed that when *Hemiclepsis* is moving towards a source of light it makes many searching movements and ultimately turns and moves away. It then makes fewer searching movements. The circumstances under which the leech was induced to move towards the light were perhaps a little unfair. A typical experiment is illustrated in Fig. 47. The leech was placed in the centre of a circular dish with a 40 W lamp at one side. It moved away on a path which made an angle of 35° with the direction of the light and eventually reached the side of the dish. It then turned and moved along the side of the dish and in doing so was induced to move towards the light. It made searching movements on five occasions before turning back from the light. While moving away from the light it made searching movements on only one occasion. When the light source was changed to 150 W it turned and retraced its steps while at a much greater distance from the light. The unsatisfactory element in this experiment is that the leech was almost certainly responding to the contact stimulus

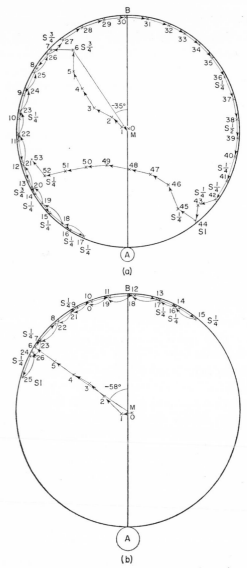

Fig. 47. The track followed by *Hemiclepsis* when placed at M, the centre of a circular dish which was illuminated by a single light source at A. In experiment (a) the light source was a 40 W lamp, in (b) a 150 W lamp. S indicates searching movements and is followed by the time in minutes for which the movements were carried out. From Herter, 1936.

from the side of the dish. It will be shown on p. 94 that leeches
are strongly thigmotactic. If it had not been for this complicating
factor the leech would probably never have moved towards the
light for any considerable distance.

Herter found that none of the leeches which he studied moved
directly away from the source of light when free to do so. *Piscicola*
moved along a path which was up to 48° from the line of the light
rays and *Hemiclepsis* up to 90°. On the other hand Gee found that
Helobdella frequently moved almost directly away from the light
source, pausing to make frequent searching movements as it did so.
Both these workers concluded that there is a very considerable
degree of random movement in the responses of leeches to light
and Herter found this surprising in view of the level of complexity
of the leech eye. Since he worked mainly with Glossiphoniidae,
which have the eyes rather far below the surface of the head, it
would be interesting to investigate the behaviour of leeches with
more superficial and more complex eyes, and to study the effects of
unilateral blinding and of varying the direction of the incident
light during the course of an experiment.

Leeches have no statocysts or other organs for orientation in
relation to gravity and it appears that when swimming they make
use of the fact that light normally falls on them from above and
exhibit a dorsal light reaction. If a swimming medicinal leech is
suddenly subjected to light from below and not from above it will
swim in a vertical arc until its dorsal side is directed towards the
light (Schluter, 1933). It does not maintain this position indefinitely, however, but eventually returns to its normal orientation, presumably in response to the effect of gravity on the internal
organs. A similar dorsal light reaction is shown by leeches placed
between two glass plates and this response is shown even by
decapitated leeches, indicating that the eyes are not essential to
the reaction, the light sensitive cells of the dorsal body wall being
sufficient.

When a shadow passes over a leech in its natural habitat it is
likely that this is caused by the movement of a larger animal. The
blood-sucking parasites often react by making searching movements, or even by swimming upwards through the water. The
non-parasitic forms react in other ways; they may flatten themselves against the substratum or abruptly cease making ventilatory

movements. In this way they are less easily seen by a predator. The reflex involving cessation of ventilatory movements is one which is particularly suited to experimental study. Common European freshwater leeches which exhibit it are *Hirudo, Haemopis* and *Erpobdella*. It is not necessary to shade the whole of the animal, for under favourable circumstances they will respond to a decrease in light intensity on a small part of the posterior sucker (Kaiser, 1954). Decapitated leeches respond just as well as intact animals, so clearly it is the epidermal light sensitive cells which mediate the response. There is no response to shading the ventral surface.

If a leech is illuminated by two lights and one of them is switched off, the fall in light intensity on the epidermis of a leech produces the same effect as a shadow. By altering the intensities of the two lamps it is possible to vary the percentage fall in light intensity. Kaiser (1954) found that *Haemopis* responded to as little as 25% decrease in light intensity. The suspension of activity did not last indefinitely, ventilatory movements were resumed after 1 or 2 min. If full illumination was then turned on, the experiment could be repeated, and this time the period of inactivity was decidedly less. With constant repetition of the experiment the period of inactivity became shorter and shorter until eventually there was no response at all to the stimulus. This habituation is illustrated in Fig. 48. With 100% reduction in light intensity the first period of quiescence was 100 sec. It soon fell to about 10 sec, where it remained for about 20 trials. After that the response quickly disappeared. When the percentage reduction in light intensity was less the rate of habituation was proportionately more rapid, so that at 30% drop in light intensity the response disappeared after only three trials.

Another reaction to light exhibited by many leeches is that of colour change. It is brought about by pigment cells in the tissues which change their appearance according to circumstances. They are much branched cells in which the pigment may be either concentrated into a small sphere in the centre of the cell, in which case the cell is very inconspicuous, or may be dispersed throughout the branches of the cell, making it conspicuous and contributing to the general colour pattern of the animal. It is the type of chromatophore found, for instance, in Crustacea and vertebrates. The

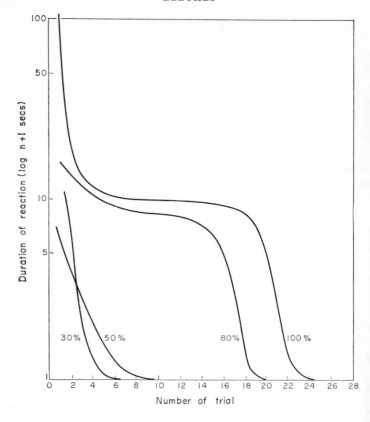

Fig. 48. Habituation in reaction to decrease in light intensity
(shadow reflex). The percentage drops in light intensity is
marked against each line. For further explanation see text.
Based on the data of Kaiser, 1954.

change from one state to the other is a relatively slow process,
usually taking about 1 hr, although the dark brown chromatophores
of *Piscicola* are exceptional and can expand in about 15 min. Most
of the leeches in which colour change has been observed are blood-
sucking parasites of vertebrates, for example *Theromyzon* and
Hemiclepsis. These become positively phototactic when hungry
and so expose themselves to predators in daylight. Presumably
the change in colour makes them less conspicuous under these

circumstances. *Glossiphonia complanata* which is not of this habit does possess variable chromatophores but they are so sparsely scattered in the tissues that they make little difference to the appearance of the animal (Wells, 1932).

Kowalewski (1900) claimed that *Placobdella costata*, a parasite of the European water tortoise, was green when resting on vegetation but brown when on a tortoise. This suggests that the leech possesses at least a rudimentary form of colour vision. Denzer-Melbrandt (1935) studied the question of colour vision in leeches. She prepared test containers in which the incident light passed through various shades of coloured paper, and she observed in a large number of trials which colours the leeches preferred. She claimed that *Helobdella* and *Hirudo* showed a preference for colours of longer wavelength, even when this involved moving into regions of higher light intensity. The method used for determining the light intensity involved making comparisons by the human eye. If the leech eyes happened to be less sensitive than the human eyes at the red end of the spectrum it is possible that they were in fact showing a preference for the zones which appeared to them to be illuminated at a lower intensity. We must therefore regard the case for the existence of colour vision in leeches as not proven.

On the other hand, Smith (1942) showed clearly that the chromatophores of *Placobdella parasitica* respond to simple changes in light intensity. This leech has three kinds of chromatophores, yellow, green and reddish brown. Of these the green are most active in colour change, expanding in light and contracting in darkness. It appears that the chromatophores are under nervous control, for electrical stimulation at either end of the body will cause a pale leech to darken, but if the nerve cord is transected the effect will not be produced beyond the cut. Decapitation causes a pale leech to darken, but after it has recovered from the shock of the operation it will still change colour slowly in response to changes in light intensity. This shows that the eyes are not essential to the process and that the light sensitive cells of the epidermis can mediate the response. In fact, if a decapitated leech is brought from darkness into the light and one part of the body is shaded that part will remain paler. Vavrouskova (1952) studied the colour change mechanism of *Theromyzon tessulatum* and concluded that the chromatophores were themselves sensitive to light and could respond to changes in light intensity without the mediation of the central nervous system.

3. REACTIONS TO HEAT

Those leeches such as *Hirudo* and *Theromyzon* which suck the blood of warm-blooded animals are stimulated to attach themselves to an object warmed to 33–35°C. *Placobdella costata* is said to be attracted to such an object from a distance of 15 cm (Mannsfeld, 1934). If the temperature is raised above 35°C *Hirudo* will eventually release its hold and in a number of trials the average temperature at which this occurred was 41·5°C. *Theromyzon* releases its hold at a similar temperature but parasites of fish let go at about 31°C while those which attack invertebrates release their hold from the tube at under 30°C (Table 4 column 5). Land leeches (*Haemadipsa*) when hungry will sit erect on their posterior suckers. If they are then subjected to a current of warm, moist air they will move towards the source of it (Stammers, 1950). A man's breath or the wind moving past his hand (if this is held a few inches from the leech) is sufficient to produce this reaction (Matthews, 1954).

When placed in a temperature gradient *Hirudo* congregated in water of 21°C and Kaiser (1954) concluded that it was capable of distinguishing between temperatures differing by only 1·5°C. When subjected to temperatures higher than those normally occurring in the natural habitat leeches show a distinct series of behaviour patterns. The first is a shock reaction, comparable with that obtained with strong tactile stimulation, in which the longitudinal muscles are strongly contracted. This occurs at temperatures between 26° and 39° according to species. In the next phase the leeches coil and uncoil vigorously, throwing themselves into a variety of contortions. At still higher temperatures locomotion becomes impossible and finally paralysis sets in. The temperatures at which the four stages were reached by various German freshwater leeches are shown in Table 4 columns 1–4. *Piscicola* showed the greatest sensitivity to rising temperatures while the greatest tolerance of high temperatures was shown by *Hirudo* and *Theromyzon*. *Piscicola* is closely related to marine

TABLE 4. COMPARATIVE TABLE OF TEMPERATURES AT WHICH LEECHES SHOWED VARIOUS REACTIONS
(Figures indicate degrees centigrade)

	1 Shock response	2 Coiling and uncoiling	3 Locomotion ceased	4 Paralysis	5 Released hold on heated tube
Hirudo medicinalis	39·0	41·0	42·0	43·5	41·5
Theromyzon tessulatum	34·5	38·5	42·5	43·5	42·0
Hemiclepsis marginata	31·0	36·0	36·5	40·0	31·0
Piscicola geometra	26·0	31·5	32·0	36·5	31·5
Glossiphonia complanata	27·0	31·0	33·0	40·0	26·0
Helobdella stagnalis	30·5	33·5	34·0	40·0	27·0
Erpobdella sp.	30·0	34·5	35·5	40·0	29·5

leeches and is not normally found in small enclosed bodies of
water where the temperature may rise excessively. *Hirudo* and
Theromyzon on the other hand do inhabit such places and must be
able to survive contact with warm blooded hosts.

When the rate of locomotion of *Hemiclepsis* was measured at

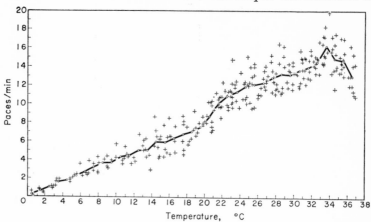

Fɪɢ. 49.   Rate of locomotion of *Hemiclepsis* in relation to
temperature. From Herter, 1932.

many temperatures it was found to increase in an almost linear
manner from 0 to 34°C after which it declined (Fig. 49). According
to Table 4 locomotion ceases at 36·5°C.

4.   Rᴇᴀᴄᴛɪᴏɴs ᴛᴏ Mᴇᴄʜᴀɴɪᴄᴀʟ Sᴛɪᴍᴜʟᴜs

One of the most characteristic reactions of leeches is their
tendency to creep into crevices, i.e. their strong positive thigmo-
taxis.   In nature freshwater leeches are most commonly found
under stones or in the leaf axils of plants.   The reaction is not
entirely one of light avoidance as is shown by the experiment in
which leeches were given the choice of remaining in the open or of
creeping under a sheet of glass where there was little reduction
of light intensity.   Table 5 shows that the majority preferred to
lie under the sheet of glass.   Here again there is a distinction
between the predators of invertebrates, such as *Glossiphonia* and
Helobdella, and the blood-sucking parasites of mammals, for the

TABLE 5.   OBSERVATIONS ON THE TENDENCY OF LEECHES TO
TAKE UP THEIR POSITION IN A CREVICE UNDER A GLASS PLATE

	Number of leeches	Number of observations	Percentage free	Percentage under glass
Glossiphonia complanata	6	120	0·0	100·0
Helobdella stagnalis	6	96	1·0	99·0
Hemiclepsis marginata	6	90	2·2	97·8
Theromyzon tessulatum (medium size)	1	16	6·2	93·7
Theromyzon tessulatum (small)	5	80	57·5	42·5
Erpobdella sp.	6	84	45·2	54·8
Hirudo medicinalis	4	52	61·5	38·5
Piscicola geometra	6	54	100·0	0·0

former were much more positively thigmotactic. The way in which hunger modifies this reaction is shown by *Theromyzon*, where the large animals with full guts were much more positively thigmotactic than smaller specimens.

Leeches are very sensitive to touch. As far as can be judged from experiments with paint brushes and needles they are most sensitive on the front of the head and least sensitive posteriorly. Large or well fed specimens are less responsive than small or hungry ones. When a *Glossiphonia* is resting in a shallow dish of water and a needle is brought towards it it responds long before the needle touches it. First there is a response when the needle touches the surface film; if it is performing undulatory movements these cease abruptly or if it is resting then it presses its body closer to the substratum. If the needle is now brought towards the margin of the body this will be withdrawn before the needle actually makes contact (Gee, 1912). In these experiments the leech is presumably reacting to vibrations in the water caused by the movement of the needle. Erpobdellids respond to vibration by rapid longitudinal contraction and parasitic forms may respond by making searching movements or even by swimming upwards in the water.

Some leeches are able to locate the centre of a disturbance in the water. Figure 50 illustrates an experiment in which *Theromyzon* reacted to a disturbance created at three different points in succession by blowing down a tube on to the surface of the water. It is obvious that it was able to direct its movements towards the source of disturbance with a fair degree of accuracy. It is also

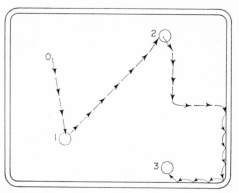

Fig. 50. The path taken by *Theromyzon* when a disturbance was created successively at 1, 2, and 3 by blowing down a tube on to the surface of the water. From Herter, 1929.

well known that *Hirudo* uses this method to locate its host, for hungry leeches will converge on a centre of disturbance in a pond in which they are living even if the disturbance is made by moving a stick rather than by any part of an animal.

5. Reactions to Gravity

Leeches have no specific organs of gravity perception yet most of them show a positive geotaxis as was shown by Herter's observations on the distribution of various species in a tall glass tube, precautions being taken to eliminate light influence. He found that *Helobdella stagnalis, Glossiphonia complanata, G. heteroclita* and *P. geometra* were resting in the lower 10 cm of the tube on more than 90% of the occasions while *Hemiclepsis marginata* and *Erpobdella* sp. showed a greater tendency to wander upwards, being found in the lowest 10 cm on just over 70% of occasions. On the other hand, hungry specimens of *Theromyzon tessulatum* and *Hirudo medicinalis* congregated near the surface of the water. Presumably the leeches detect the force of gravity from its effect on the tissues of the body.

When light and gravity responses are in conflict it is the light response that overrides the other on most occasions. When the upper half of an aquarium was shaded while the lower half was lighted specimens of *Hirudo* came to rest in the upper half on 89% of the occasions observed but when light and shade were reversed they came to rest in the lower half on 76% of the occasions. Another factor modifying geotaxis is oxygen lack, for many leeches which would otherwise remain near the bottom rise to the surface when oxygen is scarce.

6. REACTIONS TO CHEMICAL SUBSTANCES

It is recorded that *Hemiclepsis* can with difficulty be persuaded to suck blood from *Rana temporaria*, that it will never suck the blood of *Rana esculenta* but that it sucks readily on the larvae of *Pelobates*. The basis of such discrimination may be partly tactile but is almost certainly mainly chemical. Again, *Hemiclepsis* will often ignore a glass rod brought into contact with its head but if this glass rod has been rubbed on the skin of a fish it will attach itself with alacrity and attempt to suck from it. There is therefore no doubt that leeches have a well developed chemical sense.

Some authors have distinguished between taste and smell in leeches. By this they have meant the distinction between a response to chemical substances drifting in the water and a response to close contact between the surface of the animal and a particular substance. In fact there is no evidence at all that leeches have more than one kind of chemoreceptor and it is perhaps best to regard the two sensations as two aspects of the one activity.

Examples of response to substances drifting in the water are afforded by the reactions of various leeches to extracts of their normal host animals. In most cases the reaction is random and undirected; for example, if the juice of a pond snail is added to the water in a dish containing *Glossiphonia complanata* the leeches may respond by making searching movements, especially if their guts are empty, but their movements do not bring them to rest at the

centre of the cloud of snail juice (Fig. 51). *Hemiclepsis* reacts to
fish extract in a similar manner but *Piscicola* which is also a fish
parasite shows no such reaction. This is interesting in view of the
fact that *Hemiclepsis* normally lives in still water and *Piscicola* in

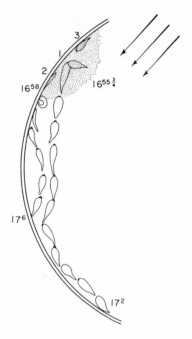

Fig. 51. Successive positions of three specimens (1, 2 and 3)
of *Glossiphonia complanata* after addition of snail extract to the
water (dotted area) at 16.55 hr. Arrows indicate direction of
light; times are in hours and minutes. Temperature, 16°C.
From Herter, 1936.

running water or the surf zones of lakes. It is unlikely that in its
natural surroundings chemical substances will stay in one place
long enough for *Piscicola* to react to them.

A detailed study of the substances which evoke a reaction in
Hirudo was made by Kaiser (1954). He placed five leeches in
200 ml of water in a dish and when they were at rest he added a
test substance drop by drop. With acids the leeches responded
by making characteristic jerking and quivering movements, while

TABLE 6.

THE REACTIONS OF *Hirudo* TO SUBSTANCES ADDED TO THE WATER

Substance (in solution where appropriate)	Amount used (1 drop = 0·04 ml)	Reaction
Formic acid	1 drop	Quivering reaction, leave water.
Acetic acid	2 drops	Weaker reaction than above. After 5 min anterior sucker out of water.
Proprionic acid	2 drops	As for acetic acid.
Iso-butyric acid	2 drops	
n-butyric acid	2 drops	Weaker reaction. Leave water after 30 sec.
Caprylic acid	Several drops	React only to one undiluted drop.
Oxalic acid	2 drops	Typical acid reaction (see text).
Malonic acid	5–10 drops	
Succinic acid	5–10 drops	
Citric acid	1 drop	
Hydrochloric acid	1 drop	
Phenol	1 drop	Shock reaction, leave the water.
Thymol	a crystal	No reaction.
Napthol	2 drops	Typical acid reaction. Soon leave water.
p-nitrophenol	a crystal	Leave water. Weak reaction.
Galactose		No reaction.
Sucrose		
Glucose		
Lactose		
Methyl alcohol		No reaction.
Butyl alcohol		
Glycerin		
Quinine		Swim about restlessly then come to rest with anterior sucker out of the water.
Caffein		
Atropine	1 drop	
Cocaine		
Morphia		
Ammonia	1 drop	Strong reaction, leave water.
Urea	a crystal	Clear reaction.
Indol	2 drops	Leave water hastily.
Skatol	a crystal	
Pyridin	1 drop	React only to undiluted substance.
Camphor	1 drop	No reaction.

various other substances evoked normal locomotory exploratory movements. Noxious substances caused the leeches to come to rest with their anterior suckers out of the water but the rest of the body still immersed. This suggests that the chemoreceptors are confined to the head so that when this part of the body is out of the water the leeches are no longer aware of the noxious stimulus. In Table 6 is given a list of the substances tested and the reactions they produced. Among the saturated fatty acids the most marked effect was produced by formic acid. Sugars and alcohols produced no effect in the concentrations used but alkaloids such as quinine and caffeine gave rise to strong reactions. Substances which might have been produced by a host animal, such as ammonia and urea, gave rise to exploratory movements and substances which are distasteful to man, such as indol and skatol, evoked a strong reaction.

The case quoted above of *Hemiclepsis* reacting to a glass rod previously rubbed on the skin of a fish is an example of contact chemoreception. Practically all the European freshwater leeches react to a suitably prepared glass rod, *Hirudo* to one which has been held under a man's armpit, *Theromyzon* to one which has been in contact with the preen gland of a duck, or *Helobdella* to one smeared with the blood of a snail. As long ago as 1916 Löhner studied the reactions of *Hirudo* to various substances mixed with its food. He persuaded the leeches to take blood by sucking at a piece of skin stretched across a glass tube. While the leeches were feeding he mixed the test substances with the blood in the tube and noticed whether they caused the leeches to stop sucking. With sodium chloride they reacted to a concentration of 7%, with sucrose at 5% but with quinine at only 0·1%. It is therefore clear that leeches have chemoreceptors which provide information about substances in the water, substances with which the anterior sucker comes in contact and substances contained in the blood which is passing through the buccal cavity.

CHAPTER 9

REPRODUCTION AND DEVELOPMENT

1. INTRODUCTION

THE reproductive processes of leeches show interesting specializations when compared with those of earthworms and other annelids. Internal fertilization is general and in the glossiphoniids there is a well developed pattern of brood care. The method by which fertilization is achieved in most families is remarkable, for the sperms are enclosed in a spermatophore which is then attached to the body wall of another leech. The sperms make their way, by a process not fully understood, through the body wall into the coelomic sinuses and thence to the ovaries. Brood care often involves the attachment of each of several dozens of embryos to the ventral body wall of the parent by a curious ectodermal ball-and-socket joint and the parent may hold the embryos under her body for many weeks, passing a current of water over them by gentle dorso–ventral undulations.

The leeches about which we have most information, the fresh-water leeches of temperate climates, usually begin to breed in spring or early summer. Breeding condition is indicated by the differentiation of the clitellum or by the fact that stores of eggs or sperm are visible through the ventral body wall. In Britain *Glossiphonia complanata*, *Helobdella stagnalis* and *Erpobdella testacea* first come into breeding condition in March, *E. octoculata* in May and *Theromyzon tessulatum* in June (Mann, 1951; 1953b; 1957a; 1957b; 1961). There has been no experimental study of the factors controlling the reproductive cycle but from field observations it is fairly clear that there is a correlation between the environmental temperature and the onset of breeding. Not only is the breeding time of a particular species later in more northerly

latitudes, a fact which might also be accounted for by differences
in day length, but it is later in higher altitudes and can be advanced
or retarded in the laboratory by appropriate changes of temperature (Leopoldseder, 1931). In a detailed study of the life history
of *Glossiphonia complanata* (Mann, 1957a) it appeared that the
onset of breeding was governed by three factors: temperature, the
density of the population and the age of the leeches. The population was living in a network of streams which ran through water-
cress beds and carried water from a spring at the foot of chalk hills
in Berkshire, England. Owing to the fact that some streams were

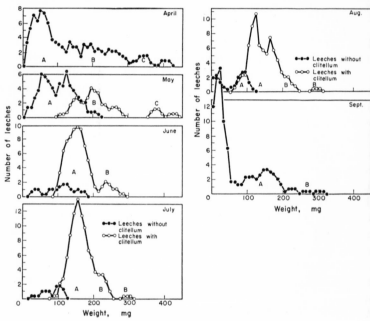

FIG. 52. The life history of *Erpobdella octoculata*. Smoothed
frequency polygons representing the distribution of weights of
leeches in 6 monthly samples of about 100, between April and
September, 1952. The weights are arranged in 10 mg classes.
Each point represents the mean value of its own class, the one
above and the one below. A, B and C indicate the same three
populations in successive samples, and in May represent 1, 2 and
3-year age groups. Those emerging from the cocoon in 1952 are
first seen in the samples in September. Note that 2-year-olds
breed before 1-year-olds. From Mann, 1953.

ieavily shaded while others were not, the diurnal rise of tempera-
ure was more marked in some streams than in others. The
oreeding activity was most advanced in the warmer waters. Within
a given section of the stream breeding was more advanced in
olaces where the leeches were densely aggregated, presumably
oecause the opportunity for fertilization was greater, or because
here was some physiological response to the presence of numbers
of other leeches. Moreover, 2-year-old leeches began breeding
about one month earlier than 1-year-olds.

Erpobdella testacea is an annual species, breeding at 1 year of

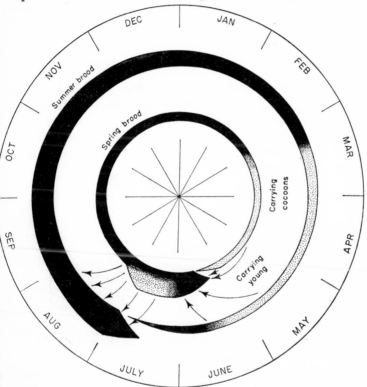

Fig. 53. Diagram of the life history of *Helobdella stagnalis* in a
calcareous artificial lake. The width of the line is roughly
proportional to the density of the population. Dotted areas
indicate breeding leeches; arrows indicate the release of young
by the parents. From Mann, 1957.

age and dying soon afterwards, but *Erpobdella octoculata* and *Glossiphonia complanata* are longer lived. Most of the leeches of these two species breed at 1 year of age, they all breed at 2 years and after that most of them die. Those that survive beyond this time are probably the ones that failed to reach maturity in the first year of life. *Helobdella stagnalis* has a life history which is different again, some of the leeches passing through two generations in 1 year. Overwintering leeches breed in spring and die soon afterwards; some of the spring brood grow to maturity that summer, breed and die, but the remainder overwinter to breed the following spring. The proportion reaching maturity in less than 1 year seems to depend on the weather (Mann, 1957b).

2. FERTILIZATION

Leeches are protandrous hermaphrodites and cross fertilization is the general rule. The Hirudidae have an eversible penis and at copulation this is inserted into the vagina of another leech. If the animals take up a head-to-tail position reciprocal fertilization is possible, but this is by no means general and unilateral action is

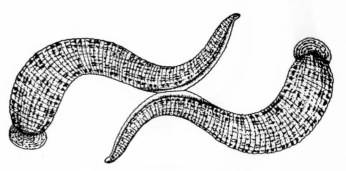

FIG. 54.   *Hirudinaria granulosa* copulating. From Bhatia, 1941.

probably more usual. Leslie (1951) described a simple courtship display by the land leech *Haemadipsa*. It involved tapping (with their anterior suckers) the leaf on which they were sitting and entwining the anterior ends of their bodies in various ways before copulating. Leeches of the families Erpobdellidae, Glossiphoniidae and Piscicolidae lack the eversible penis and transfer the sperm by means of spermatophores secreted in the terminal portion of the male duct, the atrium. The only known exception among the Glossiphoniidae is *Theromyzon tessulatum* in which the atrium can be everted in the form of a low cone which functions as a penis. Typical spermatophores are illustrated in Fig. 55. Although the

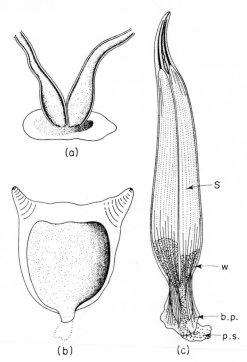

FIG. 55. Various spermatophores. (a) from *Erpobdella;* (b) from *Trachelobdella punctata;* (c) from *Placobdella parasitica. b.p.,* basal plate; *p.s.,* proteolytic substance; *s,* sperms; *w,* wall of spermatophore. From Grassé, 1959 after Brumpt (a) and (b) and Whitman (c).

shape varies greatly from one species to another they all consist of a median chamber from which originate two horns. The median chamber may be enlarged at the expense of the horns, or *vice versa,* and the horns may be widely separated as in *Erpobdella* or closely bound together as in *Glossiphonia.* The upper part of a spermatophore is packed with sperms but the lower one third usually contains a granular secretion which is thought to have proteolytic properties. The wall of the spermatophore is secreted by glands in the wall of the atrium and the sperms are pumped into it by the ejaculatory ducts. There is a base plate, perforated to allow for the passage of sperm, and when the spermatophore is expelled by the action of the muscles of the atrium walls the base plate adheres to the body of another leech.

Exchange of spermatophores is often accompanied by a close intertwining of the bodies of the leeches (Fig. 56). The clitellar

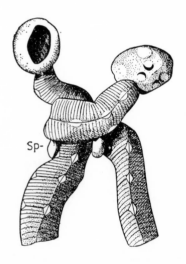

Fig. 56. *Piscicola* copulating. *sp*, spermatophore being deposited on the copulatory area. From Grassé, 1959, after Brumpt.

region is the most usual site of deposition but spermatophores are not infrequently found as far away as the dorsal region of the posterior half of the body. The most detailed study of the process of fertilization is that of Brumpt (1900). He showed that in

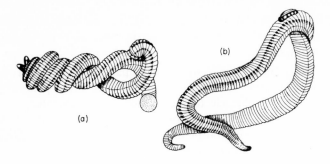

FIG. 57.   Successive positions during copulation by *Erpobdella*.
From Nagao, 1957.

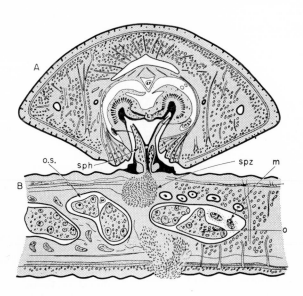

FIG. 58.   Section through two specimens, A and B, of *Erpobdella
octoculata* during implantation of the spermatophore. *m*, mass of
spermatozoa in ovary; *o*, ovarian strand; *o.s.*, ovarian sac; *sph*,
spermatophore;   *spz*,   spermatozoa.   From   Grassé,   1959,
after Brumpt.

Glossiphoniidae and Erpobdellidae the sperms pass through the epidermis into the dermal connective tissue and from there to the coelomic spaces in which the ovaries lie (Fig. 58). He favoured the view that there was no proteolytic action at the point of entry suggesting rather that the tissues were parted by the mechanical pressure of the injected fluids. The presence of a base plate would appear to be an obstacle to such action, and it therefore seems more likely that, as other authors have suggested, the granular contents of the lower end of the spermatophore have proteolytic properties. Once attached to the body of another leech, the spermatophore empties its contents into the tissues. The force required to effect the transfer is probably obtained from the wall of the spermatophore which shrink on contact with water.

In many Piscicolidae there is a special area for the reception of the spermatophore, called the copulatory area. In *Piscicola* for instance (Fig. 59) it lies behind the genital pores. Immediately

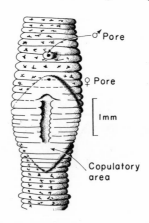

FIG. 59.   Ventral view of part of body wall of *Piscicola*, showing genital pores and copulatory area. After Brumpt, 1900.

beneath it there is a pad of fibrous connective tissue with two strands running to the ovarian sacs. It is called conducting tissue. The spermatophores are normally deposited on the copulatory area and the sperms travel most readily through the underlying fibrous connective tissue, and are conducted direct to the ovaries. In other Piscicolidae, such as *Callobdella lophii*, there are

strands of conducting tissue running from the male genital
aperture to the ovaries, so that cross fertilization can be achieved
by introduction of a spermatophore into the male genital aperture
of another leech (Fig. 61).

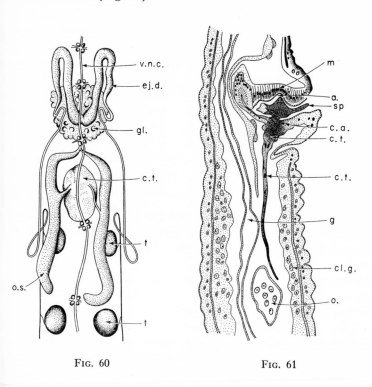

FIG. 60   FIG. 61

FIG. 60.   Reproductive organs of *Piscicola geometra*, dorsal
view. *c.t.*, conducting tissue; *ej.d.*, ejaculatory duct; *gl*, glands
secreting wall of spermatophore; *o.s.*, ovarian sac; *t*, testis sac;
v.n.c., ventral nerve cord. From Dawydoff, 1959, after Brumpt.

FIG. 61.   Sagittal section through *Cystobranchus mammillatus*
to show conducting tissue. *a*, male genital atrium; *c.a.*, copulatory area; *c.t.*, conducting tissue; *cl.g.*, clitellar glands; *g*, gut;
m, muscular wall of atrium; *o*, ovarian sac; *sp*, spermatophore.
From Grassé, 1959, after Brumpt.

3. Egg Laying and Brood Care

Once fertilization has been achieved the eggs are ready to be deposited in a cocoon. There is often a considerable delay between copulation and cocoon deposition. In the case of the Hirudidae,

Table 7. Time which may Elapse between Copulation and Cocoon Deposition

Species	Time
Erpobdella sp.	2–20 days
Glossiphonia complanata	8–21 days
Haementeria officinalis	10 days
Haemopis sanguisuga	$1\frac{1}{2}$ months
Hirudo medicinalis	1–9 months

where sperms have been introduced into the vagina directly, we must presume that the sperms are stored and fertilization is delayed, for there is no evidence that the eggs are at an advanced stage in development when they are placed in the cocoon. In other families the delay is only a matter of days and this is presumably the time taken for the sperms to migrate through the tissues after the implantation of the spermatophore.

There are two kinds of glands contributing material for the formation of the cocoon, those which secrete the outer wall material and those which secrete the albuminous fluid in which the eggs are suspended inside the cocoon. The normal arrangement is for these glands to be distributed over the whole of the body wall in the clitellar region but in a few cases which have been investigated, such as *Hemiclepsis marginata* and *Glossiphonia lata* the clitellar glands are restricted to a small area round the genital pores on the ventral side of the body. As a result, the method of cocoon formation is considerably modified. Before dealing with it let us consider the more normal method.

Erpobdellid leeches first prepare a position for cocoon deposition by applying a secretion to the substratum with a "lapping" movement of the anterior sucker. They then place the clitellum over this position and begin to secrete the cocoon. During this process

.he anterior and posterior ends of the clitellum are greatly constricted so that the cocoon is formed in a lemon shape. The inner
surface is smoothed by turning the body of the leech about its

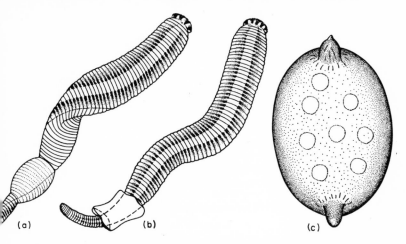

FIG. 62. *Erpobdella lineata* in process of cocoon formation.
(a) rotating the body to shape the inner wall of the cocoon;
(b) withdrawing the body by pulling backwards; (c) the cocoon.
From Nagao, 1957.

longitudinal axis and when this is done the whole of the anterior
part of the body is made as long and thin as possible by contraction
of circular muscles. Into the space left between the body of the
leech and the wall of the cocoon is passed an albuminous nutritive
fluid and a number of fertilized eggs. The anterior part of the
body is then slowly worked backwards out of the cocoon. As the
head passes the anterior and posterior apertures of the cocoon
these are sealed off by means of a plug produced by the glands of
the anterior sucker. At this stage the cocoon is a soft, translucent
and colourless bag. The leech now proceeds to flatten it into an
elliptical sac of the form shown in Fig. 63 and in a few days it
becomes dark brown, hard and almost opaque. The parent takes no
further interest.

In the Piscicolidae, Hirudidae and Haemadipsidae the process
of cocoon formation is very similar except that the cocoon is not
pressed flat but is allowed to retain its rounded shape. Moreover,

112   LEECHES

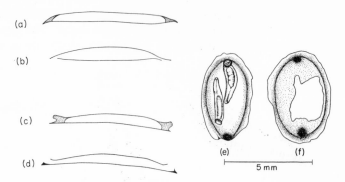

FIG. 63.   Details of cocoons of *Erpobdella*. (a) and (b) schematic longitudinal sections of the cocoon of *E. testacea* before and after the young have emerged; (c) and (d) the same for *E. octoculata* showing a different method of forming the terminal plugs; (e) cocoon of *E. octoculata* with one plug removed ready for the young to leave; (f) a cocoon emptied by a snail. From Bennike, 1943.

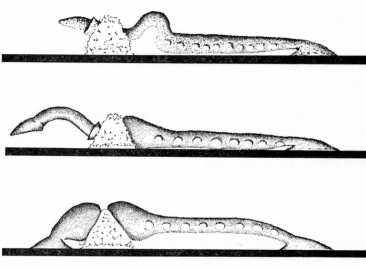

FIG. 64.   Three stages in cocoon formation by *Cystobranchus respirans*. The upper figure represents the latest stage. From Hoffmann, 1956.

he wall is usually differentiated into an outer ornamented or
spongy layer and an inner smooth layer (Fig. 65). In the case of
the Hirudidae and Haemadipsidae it is thought that one function
of the spongy layer is to reduce water loss, for members of these

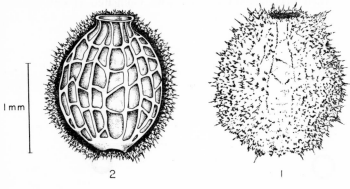

FIG. 65. Cocoons of *Cystobranchus*. *1*, complete; *2*, with
spongy layer removed from upper surface. From Hoffmann,
1955.

families lay their cocoons on land. Zick (1933) analysed the wall
of the cocoon of *Hirudo* and found that it was a scleroprotein
closely related to fibroin, a constituent of insect silk. He proposed
for it the name hirudoin.

The Glossiphoniidae are interesting for the degree of parental
care which they exhibit. They produce a very thin-walled cocoon
and immediately after deposition they place their bodies over it
and assume a protective role. Most glossiphoniids produce the
cocoon in the same manner as other leeches, secreting it as a girdle
round the body and fastening it to the substratum before backing
out of it, but in those species mentioned earlier where the clitellar
glands are confined to an area round the genital pores the cocoon
forms like a bubble over the genital pores and the eggs are dis-
charged into it. The process has recently been described and
illustrated for the Japanese leech *Glossiphonia lata* by Nagao (1958)
(Fig. 66).

At an early stage in development, while still enclosed within the
egg membrane, the young glossiphoniid leeches develop an
embryonic attachment organ. It takes the form of a knob of

elongated ectodermal cells placed near the anterior end of the
body in the mid-ventral line. The embryos, which at this stage
break free of the thin-walled cocoon, become arranged in a single
layer with their attachment organs directed upwards and each of
these then becomes interlocked with elongated epidermal cells

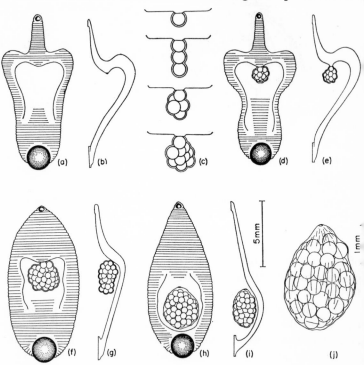

Fig. 66.   Egg laying by *Glossiphonia lata*. (a), (b) formation of
a cavity on the ventral side of the body; (c) to (g), secretion of a
saclike cocoon by a ring of clitellar glands round the genital
pore and extrusion of the eggs into the cocoon; (h), (i), cocoon
moved to a posterior position for brooding; (j), appearance of
cocoon. From Nagao, 1958.

which form a kind of socket on the parent's ventral body wall.
It has been suggested that a transfer of nutriment takes place at
this stage but on the whole this seems unlikely as the embryo is
well provided with yolk and the egg membrane is interposed
between embryo and parent.

While in this position the young leeches develop until anterior and posterior suckers are well formed and there is a nervous system capable of co-ordinating their activity. They then hatch from the egg, lose their attachment by the larval organ and hold on to the parent by their posterior suckers. In this position they may be carried about by the parent for several weeks or months, according

FIG. 67.   Young *Glossiphonia complanata* taking their first meal
of blood from an *Erpobdella*. From Pawlowski, 1955.

to the species. *Glossiphonia complanata* holds the eggs in the cocoon for 5–6 days, holds them by the embryonic attachment organ for 4–5 days and then shelters the young leeches which are holding by their posterior suckers for up to 14 days so that the whole process occupies about 24 days (Mann, 1957a). *Theromyzon tessulatum* on the other hand may hold the eggs in the capsules for

8–10 days, but then hold them under her body for nearly four months (Mann, 1951). The parent not only provides shelter but by undulating movements of her body provides the young leeches with a fresh supply of water for respiratory purposes. It has often been noticed that young leeches prematurely removed from the parent fail to survive. Since it is unlikely that they had been receiving nutriment it may well be that the ventilatory movements of the parent's body were essential to the young leeches.

The time when the young leave the shelter of the parent is probably determined mainly by the size of the store of yolk in the crop. When all this has been utilized the young leeches are ready to take their first meal. Pawlowski (1955) records what happened when the young of a *Glossiphonia complanata* took their first meal. They deserted the parent and attached themselves *en masse* to the body of a specimen of *Erpobdella octoculata*. They forced their proboscides as deeply as possible into the body wall of the *Erpobdella* and proceeded to fill their crops with its red blood. The attacked animal swam, lashed about and almost tied itself in knots in an effort to dislodge the parasites but to no avail. Their posterior suckers were free and their bodies waving freely but they retained their hold by virtue of having their proboscides embedded to the maximum depth. An *Erpobdella* may survive the attack of a small number of *Glossiphonia* but the attack of a large number is fatal.

When the young of *Theromyzon tessulatum* leave the parent, often on account of the death of the latter, they tend to remain densely aggregated until the opportunity arises to enter the nostril of a water bird. There is at least one case on record (Mann, 1951) of ducklings being killed in considerable numbers by the attacks of young *Theromyzon*. When dozens of leeches enter the nostril of a bird and there gorge on blood from the mucous membrane of the nose and throat there is danger of asphyxiation or of death from loss of blood.

4. DEVELOPMENT OF THE EGGS

The cleavage of leech eggs is basically of the spiral type. Other groups in which this method of cleavage is found include platy-helminths, nemerteans, molluscs other than cephalopods, polychaetes and oligochaetes. While there is great individual variation in both the method of cleavage and the type of larva formed, it is possible to discern a general pattern of development which runs somewhat as follows. Two divisions in a vertical plane separate

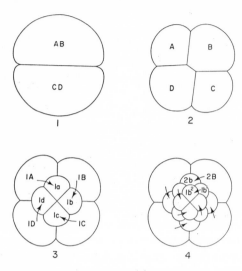

Fig. 68. Diagram illustrating spiral cleavage. From Waddington, 1956.

the fertilized egg into four blastomeres, usually of unequal size. These are conventionally known as the macromeres A, B, C and D. Each macromere then cuts off a small cell, a micromere, at one end of the egg (the animal pole) and these are named $1a$, $1b$, $1c$ and $1d$. Instead of lying immediately above the macromeres which gave rise to them the micromeres lie a little to one side owing to tilting of the cleavage spindle during division. A second set of micromeres $2a$, $2b$, $2c$ and $2d$ are now formed but when the first set are displaced clockwise the second set are displaced anticlockwise, and *vice versa*. A third set is formed and a fourth, each being offset in the opposite direction from its predecessor. While this is going on the earlier sets of micromeres themselves divide, still with their spindles tilted. In this way a hollow blastula stage is formed with a cap of micromeres surmounting four macromeres. If the latter have little yolk, gastrulation may be possible by invagination, the macromeres forming the endoderm and the micromeres the ecto-derm and mesoderm but if the macromeres are large and yolky the micromeres multiply and spread down around the outside of the macromeres bringing about gastrulation by epiboly (Fig. 69).

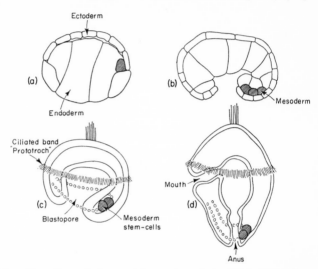

FIG. 69. Gastrulation and formation of the trochophore larva in polychaetes. (a) section through a late cleavage stage; (b) the micromeres spread over the macromeres; (c) early trochophore with mesoderm stem-cells budding off a row of mesoderm cells between the ectoderm and endoderm; (d) elongating trocho-phore with mesoderm cells taking up a vertical position. From Waddington, 1956.

The fate of each individual blastomere can be predicted accur-ately and isolated blastomeres tend to develop only into those organs which they would have formed if left undisturbed. It has therefore become usual to regard the egg as a mosaic of localized, organ-forming areas but it is a concept which must not be pushed too far, for many spirally cleaving eggs possess a limited ability to regulate the fate of the blastomeres according to circumstances.

In polychaetes the blastomere *D* is particularly important for most of the ectoderm and mesoderm of the adult worm are derived from its descendants *2d* and *4d*. *2d* is known as the somatoblast;

divides many times to form the somatic plate, an area of irregularly arranged cells which is first seen dorsally but spreads over the surface of the embryo until its edges meet ventrally (Fig. 70).

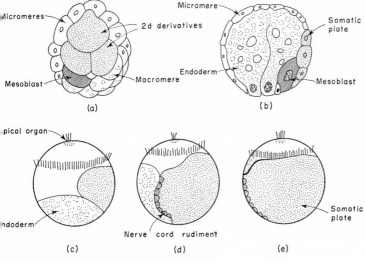

FIG. 70. Development of polychaetes. (a) blastula, showing beginnings of subdivision of *2d* to form somatic plate tissue; (b) section through slightly later stage; (c) to (e) diagrams illustrating the spread of the somatic plate tissue from dorsal to ventral side of the embryo. (a) after Child, 1900; (b) after Wilson, 1932; (c) to (e) after Dawydoff, 1959.

From the somatic plate are formed the ventral nerve cord and most of the trunk ectoderm. *4d* is known as the mesoblast and at the time of gastrulation it sinks below the surface of the embryo. It divides once and its descendants then bud off long chains of cells which eventually form the segmented mesoderm. It is usual for polychaetes to pass through a free-swimming trochophore larva stage, the organization of which is basically that of a triploblastic coelomate.

The oligochaetes, many of which are terrestrial and which deposit their eggs in a nutritive fluid enclosed within a cocoon, have lost the free swimming larval stage. Moreover, the pattern of cleavage is often so much modified that it is difficult to detect any resemblance to the polychaete pattern of spiral cleavage. The aquatic forms are the least modified and in *Tubifex* four quartette of micromeres are formed in a fairly typical manner. Instead of 2 giving rise to a plate of irregularly arranged cells it divides in regular manner to give four mother cells on each side of the embryo. These then proceed to bud off four rows of cells on each side, forming prominent longitudinal bands often called the germinal bands. Beneath these superficial rows of cells are rows of mesodermal cells budded off from the descendants of *4d*, much as in polychaetes. The germinal bands are at first situated fairly near to the dorsal side and are separated one from the other only by a small cap of micromeres (Fig. 71) but when the micromeres

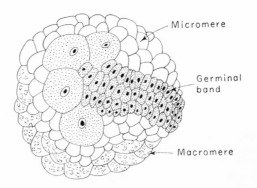

FIG. 71.   Lateral view of embryo of *Tubifex* to show one of the
two germinal bands. After Penners, 1923.

begin to multiply the germinal bands are pushed before them towards the ventral surface of the embryo and at the time of closure of the blastopore the germinal bands meet one another along the mid-ventral line. The inner row of cells from each side gives rise to the ventral nerve cord and the other rows form first the circular musculature and later the ectoderm of the adult worm, replacing the embryonic ectoderm formed from the micromere cap. The presence of these regularly arranged longitudinal rows of cells budded off from four mother cells on each side is a feature which distinguishes oligochaete embryos from those of polychaetes and

e shall see that in this feature as in many others the Hirudinea
esemble the oligochaetes.

  In terrestrial oligochaetes the formation of the germinal bands
roceeds much as in *Tubifex* but the formation of quartettes of
nicromeres and of the endoderm is frequently modified by the
ailure of two of the four original blastomeres to take any part in
evelopment. In *Bimastus* for instance blastomeres *A* and *B* form
o micromeres. *B* divides once, *A* not at all and these cells lie at
ne animal pole for a considerable period before finally degenerating.

  Against this background of annelid embryology we may turn to
he embryology of leeches. In general the Glossiphoniidae have
he least modified type of spiral cleavage and have relatively large
mounts of yolk, while the eggs of other families show greater
eviations from the typical pattern of spiral cleavage and have less
olk, relying more on the supply of albuminous fluid contained
vithin the cocoon.

5. EMBRYOLOGY OF A GLOSSIPHONIID LEECH

The egg of a glossiphoniid is about 0·5–1·0 mm in diameter and
 often coloured green or yellowish by the yolk. First and second
olar bodies are cut off in the first hour or two after the eggs have

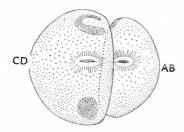

FIG. 72. Egg of *Theromyzon tessulatum* at 2-cell stage showing
pole plasm. From Dawydoff, 1959, after Schmidt.

een laid and soon afterwards two masses of clear cytoplasm, the
ole plasms, become differentiated at the animal and vegetable
oles. The animal pole plasm has a ring formation and the
egetative pole plasm is disc-shaped. The first cleavage is into

two unequal blastomeres, *AB* being smaller than *CD* and subsequent divisions in *CD* precede those in *AB*. Blastomere *D* is larger than *C* and contains most of the pole plasm. The first set of micromeres is offset in a clockwise direction when viewed from the animal pole (Fig. 73) and the second set in an anticlockwise direction. The cleavage of the egg of *Theromyzon* is particularly interesting because the pattern of spiral cleavage is so like that of

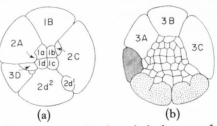

(a)   (b)

FIG. 73. (a) early stage in the spiral cleavage of an egg of *Glossiphonia complanata* viewed from animal pole; (b) later stage, showing cap of micromeres, mother cells of germinal bands (dotted) and mesoblast (hatched). After Müller, 1932.

polychaetes that Schmidt (1917) was able to recognize the cells of the "apical rosette" and the "annelid cross". This is unusual because the formation of such a regular pattern is normally prevented by the precocious cleavage of the *D* blastomere but it is usually possible in the eggs of Glossiphoniidae to follow the formation of four complete sets of micromeres much as in *Tubifex*. The micromere *2d* stands out from the others because it is usually as large as the macromere *2D*. *2d* divides several times, cutting off a number of small cells destined to join the micromere cap, and then forms eight equal sized cells. These are the mother cells of eight rows which are budded off to form germinal bands (Fig. 74).

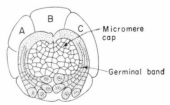

FIG. 74. Late cleavage stage of *Glossiphonia* showing germinal bands. After Whitman, 1878, modified.

As in oligochaetes these rows of cells grow forward from a postero–dorsal position forming prominent ridges at the junction of the micromere cap and the macromeres. At the same time two rows of mesoderm cells are formed beneath them. They are developed from a pair of mesoblasts which in this instance result from the division of *3D* and are therefore *4D* and *4d*. This state of affairs is different from anything found in either polychaetes or oligo-chaetes, for in these groups it is *4d* which gives rise to the right and left mesoblasts, while *4D* contributes to the endoderm. In the Glossiphoniidae there is no contribution to the endoderm from any cell of the *D* quadrant.

At this stage we have a blastula which consists of a mass of micromeres at the animal pole, three macromeres at the vegetative pole and between them on each side a ridge, comprising four superficial and one deep row of cells, the germinal band and its underlying mesoderm. The micromeres of the fourth quartette sink in and join the macromeres, which are destined to form the endoderm, but the micromeres of the first three quartettes begin

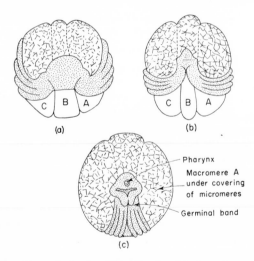

Fig. 75. Gastrulation in *Glossiphonia*. (a) the micromere cap is beginning to spread towards the vegetative pole while the germinal bands move before it; (b) a more advanced stage; (c) the two germinal bands have almost met ventrally. All viewed from the anterior end. After Whitman, 1878, modified.

to proliferate and spread from the animal pole towards th
vegetative pole. The germinal bands move before them. At thi
stage they are seen as two arcs arising from a group of eight cell
at the posterior end of the embryo and running on each side t
meet anteriorly. As the micromere cap grows and spreads the tw
germinal bands move towards the vegetative pole. Their anterio
and posterior points of union remain almost stationary and the tw
semi-circular germinal bands rotate about these points and ar
brought together in the mid-ventral line like the jaws of a trap. Th
micromeres continue to grow ventrally, finally moving over the top
of the germinal bands to meet at the vegetative pole and thus effec
the closure of the blastopore. As in the oligochaetes, the tw
median ventral rows of cells of the germinal bands form the ventra

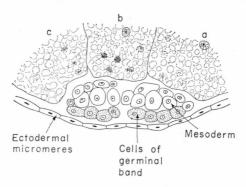

Fig. 76. Transverse section through ventral part of a *Glossiphonia* embryo after the micromeres have covered the germinal
bands; a, b, c macromeres. After Bürger, 1902.

nerve cord while the others form the circular musculature. Th
deeper row of mesodermal cells forms the somites. In the Glossi
phoniidae, but not in other families, the micromeres which hav
spread over the surface of the gastrula form the definitive epi
dermis, the descendants of the first quartette covering the head
those of the second and third the trunk.

During the next phase of development the main organs of the
body are differentiated. The ventral nerve cord, as we have seen
originates from the ventral edges of the germinal bands, bu
opinions differ about the origin of the cerebral ganglia. Dawydof

1959) favours the view that in Glossiphoniidae they are formed from the head ectoderm quite separately from the ventral nerve cord. If this is so, the situation is comparable with that found in

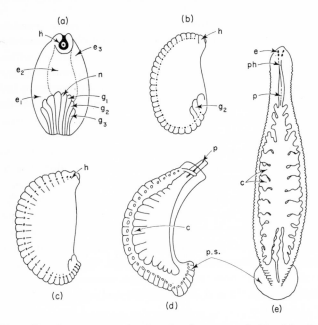

FIG. 77.   Later stages in the development of *Glossiphonia*. (a) dorsal view of an embryo a little older than that shown in 75c; (b), (c) and (d) stages in the appearance of somites and ganglia in lateral view; (e) dorsal view of a young leech ready to leave the parent; *c*, crop diverticulum; *e*, eye; e_1–e_3, endodermal macromeres seen through ectoderm; g_1–g_3, three outer rows of cells of germinal bands; *h*, head; *n*, inner row of cells of germinal band which forms nerve cord; *p*, proboscis; *ph*, pharynx; *p.s.*, posterior sucker. After Whitman, 1878.

polychaetes where the brain and prostomial organs are derived from the apical organ of the trochophore larva and not from the ventral plate.

The gut is formed from macromeres *4A*, *4B*, *4C* and the fourth quartette of micromeres. At first the endoderm is a syncytium, the nuclei dividing faster than the cytoplasm. Later the nuclei become arranged around the periphery of the yolky mass. The

yolk is slowly withdrawn from the centre to form a lumen sur
rounded by a gut epithelium and an opening to the outside world
is acquired when ectodermal cells sink in to form a stomodaeum
The proctodaeum is formed last of all.

While this is in progress the mesodermal tissue beneath the
germinal bands is dividing up into segmental blocks, beginning a
the anterior end. The blocks hollow out to form the coelom and
spread laterally round the gut, giving rise to gut musculature and
longitudinal muscles of the body wall, but in addition many mesen
chyme cells are budded off both inwards and outwards from the
walls of the coelomic sacs and septa break down to bring the
coelomic cavities into communication one with the other. Eventu
ally the coelom becomes almost obliterated and is represented only
by four longitudinal channels, two lateral, one dorsal and one
ventral, together with a complex system of transverse channels
In Glossiphoniidae blood vessels are formed mid-dorsally and
mid-ventrally but they do not develop a full set of segmenta
branches, remaining instead as rather small longitudinal vessels
totally enclosed within the dorsal and ventral coelomic channels

Nephridia are formed in two parts: the funnels and glandular
parts are formed from nephridioblasts which are intersegmenta
in position (Figs. 78 and 79) while the end sacs and ducts to the

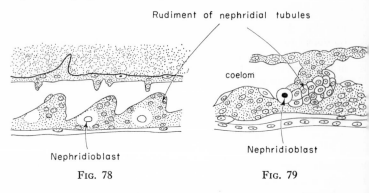

FIG. 78. Longitudinal section showing the coelom, rudimentary
septa and nephridioblasts of *Glossiphonia*. After Bychowsky,
1921.

FIG. 79. Nephridial rudiment in *Erpobdella*. From Bürger,
1891.

exterior are formed from ectodermal tissue. The question of whether the nephridioblast is ectodermal or mesodermal in origin has not been finally settled. It may well be cut off very early from ectomesoderm.

Testes differentiate from the inner walls of the coelomic sacs while these are still intact in such a way that each testis sac encloses a small part of the coelom. At a later stage the vasa efferentia arise as evaginations of the testis sacs. They join together to form the vas deferens of each side and these in turn unite with the genital atrium which has differentiated from the somatopleure anteriorly. A pair of ovarian sacs forms just behind the genital atrium. They are first seen as a pair of gonoblasts cut off from the walls of coelomic sacs and looking very like nephridioblasts. Each gonoblast divides once and one of the cells thus formed divides many times to form a group of cells which are organized into a capsule surrounding the other cell. By elongation of the capsule and subdivisions of the internal cell an ovarian sac is formed with an ovarian strand inside it and a duct to the exterior.

The segmentation of the mesoderm imposes a pattern of annulation on the epidermis and circular muscles. At first there is only one annulus per segment but soon a second annulus is cut off from the posterior border of each original one. Then another is cut off on the anterior border, giving the triannulate condition characteristic of the majority of Glossiphoniidae.

6. EMBRYOLOGY OF A GNATHOBDELLID LEECH

The gnathobdellid leech which has been most often studied is *Erpobdella*. The eggs are small and contain little yolk. The cleavage follows the normal annelid pattern up to the formation of the first quartette of micromeres. After this the blastomeres *1A* and *1B* become passive and produce no more micromeres. *1C* divides to form *2C* and *2c* and then it too becomes inactive. *2c* passes into the blastocoel and only *1D* continues to divide. Its next cleavage produces two cells of about equal size, *2d* and *2D*. The latter cuts off two more micromeres, *3d* and *4d* and these join *2c* in the blastocoel. At this stage the first quartette of micromeres occupies the animal pole, macromere *4D* is at the vegetative pole and around the equator *1A*, *1B* and *2C* occupy left, anterior and

right sides respectively, while the large micromere *2d* lies posteriorly (Fig. 80). *2d* divides three times to form eight cells, four
on each side in the postero-dorsal position, and these are the
mother cells destined to bud off the longitudinal rows of cells

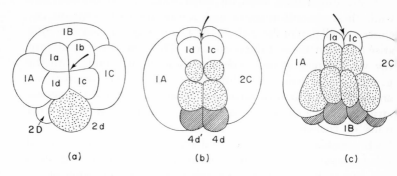

FIG. 80.   Segmentation in the egg of *Erpobdella*. The mother
cells of the germinal bands are dotted, the mesoblasts hatched.
The arrow points to the animal pole. (a) 9-cell stage viewed
from the animal pole;   (b) 16-cell stage from the D-quadrant;
(c) 23-cell stage in dorsal view. (a) after Sukatschoff, 1903;
(b) and (c) after Dimpker, 1917.

comprising the germinal bands. *4d* divides once to form a pair
of mesoblasts and these eventually bud off rows of cells for the
segmental mesoderm.

Thus in a gnathobdellid, as in a glossiphoniid leech, the germ
bands are derived from *2d* and the mesoblasts are derived from a
macromere of the *D* quadrant. The peculiar feature of the
development of a gnathobdellid leech is that the macromeres *A*, *B*
and *C* become inactive after cutting off one or two micromeres.
They do not form the endoderm for this is derived from the
micromeres *2c*, *3d* and *4d* which pass into the blastocoel at an early
stage. Almost the whole of the rest of the adult leech is derived
from the cells *2d* and *4D*, so that with the exception of the
micromere *2c* in the endoderm, the whole of the adult animal is
derived from the *D* quadrant.

Another difference between gnathobdellids and glossiphoniids
is that whereas the glossiphoniids completely lack a larval stage,
the gnathobdellids form larval organs which are discarded at

metamorphosis. The larva (Fig. 81) never has a free swimming existence but it is adapted to living in a pool of albuminous fluid within the cocoon and absorbing nutriment from it. The larval organs are formed during gastrulation. The micromeres of the

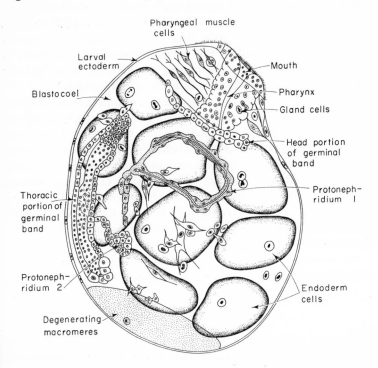

FIG. 81. Crypto-larval stage of *Erpobdella*. From Grassé, 1959, based on Bergh.

first quartette proliferate and spread from the animal pole down to the vegetative pole covering the germinal bands and closing off the blastopore. These cells form a delicate larval ectoderm, ciliated in the mid-ventral line, and a lining to the larval pharynx. The larva is also equipped with temporary pharyngeal musculature and with two to four pairs of protonephridia. It has no anus and the central nervous system is still rudimentary, but albumen is wafted into the gut by ciliary action and is used for growth in size and complexity.

At metamorphosis the larval ectoderm together with some underlying muscular and connective tissues and the protonephridia
degenerate and are replaced by tissues derived from the germinal
bands. The adult gnathobdellid is thus formed almost entirely
from germinal band and mesodermal tissue. In the larval stage
the bands are divided on each side into an anterior cephalic portion
and a posterior trunk portion (Fig. 81). The latter gives rise to
the ventral nerve cord in the normal manner but the brain is
formed from the cephalic portion of the germinal bands and not
from the larval head ectoderm as in the glossiphoniids.

The endoderm, at first represented by a number of large discrete
cells, soon takes on the form of a syncytial gut epithelium by the
fusion of the cells and the subdivision of the nuclei. It does not
become divided into separate epithelial cells until a few days after
the leeches have left the cocoon, and up to this time the gut lumen
is filled with albuminous fluid. The formation of the proctodaeum
takes place after the shedding of the larval organs. The passive
macromeres A, B and C come to lie between the gut wall and the
ectoderm in the posterior part of the embryo, where they gradually
degenerate and are absorbed.

Schoumkine (1953) has shown that in all important respects the
embryology of *Hirudo* corresponds with that of *Erpobdella*.

7. SPECIAL FEATURES OF PISCICOLID EMBRYOLOGY

Eggs of piscicolid leeches cleave normally until after the
formation of the second quartette of micromeres but subsequent
development is complicated by precocious gastrulation. The events
which occur during development are basically similar to those
occurring in other groups but the timing is quite different. At the
stage when two quartettes have been formed all micromeres except
2d begin to multiply and their descendants spread rapidly over the
other cells providing a complete covering of very flat ectodermal
cells (Fig. 82). Within this outer covering the macromeres and *2d*
continue to divide, *2d* giving rise to the mother cells of a pair of
germinal bands and *4d* forming a pair of mesoblasts. As the
original egg contained very little yolk the macromeres are quite
small. They organize themselves into a solid mass, multiply and
then form a hollow organ which is the gut rudiment (Fig. 83). At

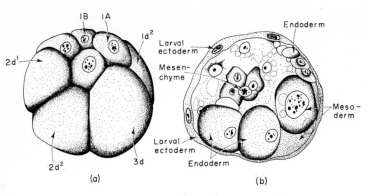

FIG. 82. (a) segmentation of egg of *Piscicola*. (b) vertical section illustrating precocious gastrulation in *Piscicola*. From Dawydoff, 1959, after Schmidt.

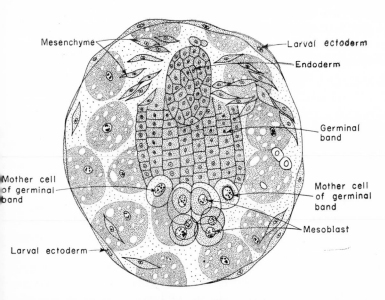

FIG. 83. Dorsal view of embryo of *Piscicola* showing endodermal gut rudiment and formation of germinal bands after precocious gastrulation. From Grassé, 1959, after Schmidt.

this stage there is a large fluid-filled space within the covering of ectodermal cells and the gut rudiment is small, occupying only a fraction of the available space. However, it soon acquires an opening to the exterior and begins to absorb nutriment from the fluid in the cocoon. This enables the endodermal cells to grow and divide until the gut occupies the greater part of the embryo (Fig. 84).

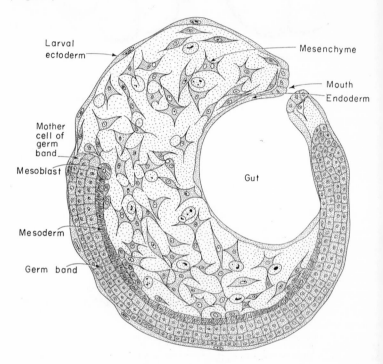

FIG. 84. Sagittal section of advanced embryo of *Piscicola*, showing the germinal bands and developing gut. From Dawydoff, 1959, after Schmidt.

While this has been going on the germinal bands have become well developed and the embryo possesses essentially the same structures as are present in the embryos of other groups after gastrulation: a gut with a stomodaeum but not a proctodaeum; a pair of germinal bands destined to give rise to the nervous system, he circular muscles and the definitive epidermis; two rows of mesodermal cells destined to form the somites; an endodermal sac which will eventually form the crop and intestine of the adult leech. Subsequent development is by way of a larva equipped with a ciliated larval ectoderm, a temporary larval pharynx and proton-ephridia. At metamorphosis these are lost, just as in the gnathobdellids.

The Piscicolidae occupy in respect of their development a position intermediate between the Glossiphoniidae and the Gnathobdellae. They share with the former an unspecialized pattern of cleavage in which all four quadrants contribute to the final animal but resemble the latter in possessing a larval stage with larval organs which are shed at metamorphosis. In the Glossiphoniidae the eggs carry a large store of yolk which enables them to complete their development without absorbing nutriment from the fluid in the cocoon, while in the Piscicolidae and Gnathobdellae there is little yolk and there is a larval stage adapted to the absorption of nutriment from the fluid in the cocoon.

8. PHYLOGENETIC CONSIDERATIONS

Whereas in polychaetes external fertilization and a free swimming larva is normal, most earthworms and leeches have evolved a habit of enclosing the fertilized eggs in a thick-walled cocoon filled with nutritive fluid. This frees the parent from the necessity of providing the eggs with a large supply of yolk, for nutriment can be absorbed as development proceeds. Schmidt (1944) considers that the habit has arisen by parallel evolution in the terrestrial oligochaetes, the gnathobdellid and the piscicolid leeches. In each case this method of rearing the eggs has resulted in a number of embryonic adaptations, particularly in the formation of a larval pharynx, an ectodermal ciliary apparatus for passing nutriment into the gut rudiment and larval nephridia. The fact that the adaptations are arrived at in a different way in each group points to an independent origin in each. The glossiphoniid leeches lack these adaptations and we may consider whether this state has been achieved by simplification or is primitive. In favour of the first view is the presence of a ciliated larva in the polychaetes. This might suggest that while the other

annelids have retained a simplified form of ciliated larva the
glossiphoniids have progressed further and suppressed it entirely
On the other hand it is among the Glossiphoniidae that we fine
a pattern of cleavage most closely resembling that of the polychaetes and Schmidt (1944) takes this to mean that the Glossiphoniidae are a primitive group of leeches and that they neve
evolved the thick-walled cocoon and its attendant larval adaptations. The peculiarities of the cleavage process in Gnathobdellac
and Piscicolidae are seen by Schmidt as preliminary stages
in the development of special larval organs.

9. EVOLUTIONARY HISTORY OF LEECHES

While we are on the subject of phylogeny it is worth while to
draw together the various lines of evidence for the relationships of
the various groups of leeches. Wendrowsky (1928) determined
the chromosome number in various species. These are listed in
Table 8. They suggest that the primitive diploid number is 1€

TABLE 8

Species	Diploid number of chromosomes
Acanthobdella peledina	16
Theromyzon tessulatum	16
Glossiphonia heteroclita	16
Glossiphonia complanata	26
Hemiclepsis marginata	32
Piscicola geometra	32
Erpobdella octoculata	16
Dina lineata	18
Haemopis sanguisuga	26

and that *Theromyzon*, which has a primitive pattern of development is also primitive in its chromosome number while *Piscicola*
which has a specialized mode of development appears to be a
tetraploid.

Another line of evidence is from the number of annuli per

segment. Oligochaetes have one annulus per segment and leeches pass through the uniannulate condition during development so it is reasonable to infer that a small number of annuli is a primitive feature. Once again it is the Glossiphoniidae with three annuli per segment which appear to be the primitive group. Next come the Gnathobdellae with five as the typical number and lastly the Piscicolidae where more than five is common (*Piscicola* has fourteen).

It seems unlikely that the Hirudinea as a whole are polyphyletic for it would be difficult to explain how more than one line of evolution arrived at 33 segments as the optimum number. If we therefore assume a common ancestral stock it is obvious that there was an early and fundamental divergence between the Rhynchobdellae and the Gnathobdellae according to whether the method of sucking blood was by a proboscis or by jaws. Within the Rhynchobdellae there is abundant evidence for regarding the

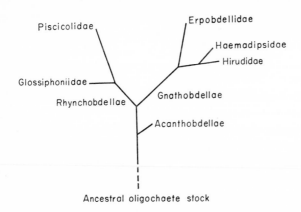

FIG. 85. Diagram illustrating the evolution of the main families of leeches from the ancestral oligochaete stock.

Glossiphoniidae as primitive and the Piscicolidae as specialized. In the Gnathobdellae it is likely that those forms with well developed jaws are primitive and that those which have become carnivorous have done so secondarily. Using this evidence it is possible to construct the evolutionary tree illustrated in Fig. 85.

CHAPTER 10

ECOLOGY

1. RELATIONS WITH THE INANIMATE ENVIRONMENT

IN THIS chapter we shall consider the ways in which the distribution and abundance of leeches is affected by factors of the environment, both living and non-living. We may begin by considering the inanimate environment, the characteristics of which have the advantage of being more easily measurable. With few exceptions leeches live in aquatic habitats. The exceptions fall into two groups, the land leeches which live in damp situations like tropical jungle and feed from time to time on passing terrestrial animals (Haemadipsidae, p. 32), and amphibious leeches which leave the water for part of the year to live in soil or under stones, feeding on worms or slugs which they swallow whole (e.g. *Trocheta* and *Haemopis*). The remainder, the truly aquatic leeches, show a pattern of distribution which may be correlated with the physical and chemical characteristics of the water. There have been four main studies of the ecology of leeches in Europe. Pawlowski (1936) and Sandner (1951) worked in Poland, Bennike (1943) in Denmark and Mann (1955) in Britain. Ten species of leech were common to all three areas so there is a good body of knowledge on the ecology of European leeches. For descriptive purposes it is convenient to divide freshwater lakes and ponds into hard, intermediate and soft waters with dividing lines at calcium concentrations of about 24 mg/l and 8 mg/l. These calcium figures give a fair indication of the total amounts of dissolved solids in the water and at the levels mentioned it has been shown that there are marked changes in the composition of the fauna of fresh waters (Ohle, 1934; Boycott, 1936). In hard waters the most abundant leech is almost always *Helobdella stagnalis* and the same is true in the intermediate group, provided that the body of water is a reasonably large one. Small ponds have different fauna (see below). Accompanying *Helobdella*, but in smaller numbers, one finds *Erpobdella octoculata, Glossiphonia complanata* and *G. heteroclita, Hemiclepsis marginata* and *Theromyzon tessulatum*. The most abundant leech in soft waters is normally *Erpobdella octoculata*, alone or accompanied by small numbers of *Helobdella, Glossiphonia complanata* or *Theromyzon*. The change from a leech fauna dominated by *Helobdella* to one dominated by *Erpobdella* is illustrated in Fig. 86.

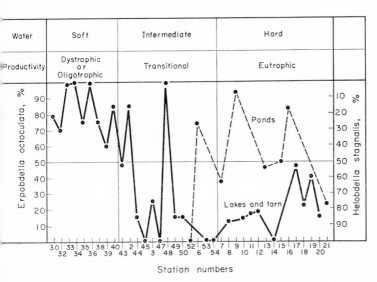

FIG. 86. The relative numbers of *Erpobdella octoculata* and *Helobdella stagnalis* in different types of standing water. Collecting stations are arranged in order of total alkalinity. The dotted line connects stations of a surface area less than 5000 square yards. From Mann, 1955.

As was stated above small bodies of water tend to have a different fauna from large ones having the same calcium content. One feature in which they differ is in the amount of rooted vegetation relative to the volume of water. Small ponds have a large proportion of rooted plants and the products of their decay lead to a high concentration of " humic acids " in the water (Tucker, 1958). The effect of this accumulation, either directly or indirectly, is to prevent *Helobdella* thriving in bodies of water which otherwise appear favourable. In soft waters the same process leads to acid dystrophic conditions which may exclude all species of leech.

The distribution of certain leeches may also be correlated with the dissolved oxygen content of the water. This factor fluctuates diurnally and annually, but it is obvious that on average the oxygen concentration is higher in unpolluted running water and on the wave-washed shores of lakes than it is in sheltered ponds having accumulations of decaying organic matter. It has been shown (p. 59) that *Erpobdella testacea* is better able to maintain aerobic metabolism in poorly oxygenated water than is *E. octoculata* and it is probable that this factor determines which of the two

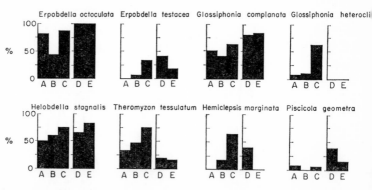

Fig. 87. The frequency of occurrence of various leeches in the different types of habitat. A, soft standing water; B, intermediate; C, hard standing water; D, slowly running water; E, fast running water; ordinates, percentage of stations within each group which contains the leech in question. From Mann, 1955.

species is the more abundant in a particular type of habitat. *E. testacea* builds up dense populations in shallow, swampy situations having a rich accumulation of decaying plant material (Mann 1959, 1960). In all probability dissolved oxygen plays a part in determining which of the two fish parasitic leeches is present in a given habitat. *Piscicola geometra* has a relatively high rate of oxygen uptake which is depressed by low oxygen concentration in the water (p. 57) and it occurs mainly in fast flowing streams and on the wave-washed shores of lakes. *Hemiclepsis* on the other hand is found chiefly in standing water or in slowly running rivers.

Some species of leech are better adapted to life in a strong current of water than others. All are equipped with suckers and so are hardly likely to be washed away in the normal course of events, but during the breeding season some species are better equipped to protect the eggs and young from being washed away and lost. *Erpobdella octoculata* produces a low, smooth cocoon, firmly fastened to a stone or plant and this species is always to be found in running water. *Glossiphonia complanata* produces a soft, gelatinous cocoon, but this is cemented down and the leech protects it with its body. This works well, and *G. complanata* is sometimes the most abundant species, especially in chalk streams. *G. heteroclita* on the other hand does not cement its cocoon to the substratum, but holds it loosely under its body. This may be the reason why flourishing populations of this species are never found in situations exposed to a current of any strength.

2.   RELATIONS WITH THE ANIMATE ENVIRONMENT

It seems that only in Europe have leeches been studied intensively so that conclusions can be reached about their habitat preferences. For the rest of the leech fauna of the world our information is mainly confined to brief notes about the food organisms with which the leech is associated, with perhaps some information about the habitats in which occasional specimens have been found. A comprehensive list of the leeches of the world with their hosts or food organisms is beyond the scope of this book, but in Table 9 this information is given for a number of better known genera. Here again the information from European sources is the more reliable since many doubts have been resolved by the careful serological, chemical and haemocytometric studies of the gut contents of leeches by Jung (1955).

Only a few leeches are restricted to one kind of host. *Hemibdella soleae* is restricted to *Solea* spp. and *Callobdella lophii* feeds only on the angler fish, *Lophius piscatorius*, but the majority of leeches, while disposed to attack a particular kind of host, such as birds or bony fish, will take a meal where they can find one. *Hirudo*, for example, while predominantly an ectoparasite of mammals, is

TABLE 9.

Species	Blood sucking on:										Devouring:				
	Mammals	Birds	Reptiles	Amphibians	Bony fish	Elasmobranchs	Molluscs	Insects	Crustaceans	Worms	Molluscs	Insects	Crustaceans	Worms	Carrion
Hirudidae															
Hirudo	x	x	x	x	x									?	
Macrobdella	x			x	x										
Philobdella	x														
Hirudinaria	x														
Haemopis											x	x	x	x	×
Erpobdellidae															
Erpobdella											x	x	x	x	×
Trocheta											x	x	x	x	
Nephelopsis												x	x	x	×
Dina												x	x	x	×
Haemadipsidae															
Haemadipsa	x			x										?	
Glossiphoniidae															
Glossiphonia							x	?	?						
Batracobdella				x			x								
Hemiclepsis				x	x										
Theromyzon		x													
Helobdella							x	x	x	x					
Haementeria	x	x	x	x											
Piscicolidae															
Piscicola					x										
Cystobranchus					x										
Pontobdella						x									
Branchellion					x	x									
Abranchus					x										

reported as sucking blood from snakes, tortoises, frogs and even fish, especially when young. The very young may even swallow small worms. It is thus very difficult to draw a sharp distinction between parasites and predators among the leeches. Not only do their habits vary during the life history of an individual, but their effect on the host may vary according to its size. Thus the Glossiphoniidae which have a proboscis and are equipped for sucking blood may suck the entire body fluids from a small snail and even finish the job by sucking up all the soft parts of the animal. This is clearly predation, but young specimens of the same species may live for long periods inside the mantle cavity of a large snail taking only occasional meals of blood, a mode of life which may reasonably be called parasitism.

Compared with the blood-sucking leeches the macrophagous forms take an even wider variety of food. Most of them will take any kind of proteinaceous material that is offered, including carrion or young of their own species. In fact Jung (1955) concluded that the only consideration is particle size. In practice the habits of the leech determine the food available to it, so that *Trocheta subviridis* which burrows in moist soil will most often encounter earthworms and slugs, while *Nephelopsis* which remains in water is particularly attracted to the corpses of fish and frogs. Similarly the American species *Macrobdella decora* will attack fish or swallow the eggs of frogs or salamanders in spite of its clear adaptations to piercing the skin of mammals (Cargo, 1960). When comparing the distribution of sanguivorous and carnivorous leeches we find that while the former have patterns of distribution related to those of their normal host organisms, the latter, which are more catholic in their tastes, have distribution patterns which are more closely related to physical and chemical features of the environment.

Feeding relationships are not the only ones which we should consider when dealing with the relations between leeches and the animate environment. Leeches also act as hosts to other parasitic forms and as vectors in the life cycles of parasites of other animals. In common with most other invertebrates leeches have their quota of endoparasitic Protozoa. Of these, some, such as *Entamoeba aulastomi* from the gut of *Haemopis* or *Orcheobius herpobdellae* from the testes of *Erpobdella* are specific to the leeches but others

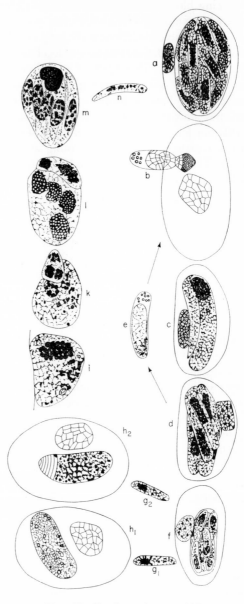

FIG. 88. See legend on p. 143.

such as *Entamoeba ranarum* occur in a variety of aquatic animals. Possibly of greater interest are the parasites for which leeches are the intermediate host by reason of their blood-sucking habits. Many species of *Trypanosoma* from the blood of freshwater fishes are transmitted by *Piscicola* and *Hemiclepsis*, and a similar role is played by *Pontobdella* and *Trachelobdella* in respect of marine fish. In these cases reinfection of the fish occurs during blood sucking, the infective stages migrating to the proboscis. Barrow (1953, 1958) in an intensive study of the biology of *Trypanosoma diemyctyli*, which has the newt *Triturus* as its primary host and the leech *Batracobdella picta* as its secondary host, showed that the passage of the infection from mother to offspring in the leech takes place via the vertebrate host. When the young leave the mother to take their first meal of vertebrate blood they may stay on the newt for 7–14 days. During this time the newt becomes infected by the mother and the trypanosomes are picked up by the offspring during feeding. Haemogregarines may also be carried by leeches, *Haemogregarina stepanowi* of the pond tortoise *Emys orbicularis* being transmitted by *Placobdella costata*.

When handling *Erpobdella octoculata* it is often possible to see numerous clear cysts in the mesenchyme or body wall. These were called tetracotyles, one kind being given the name *Tetracotyle typica*. Subsequently it was shown that they were metacercariae of strigeid trematodes, and Szidat (1930) showed that they develop, when the leeches are eaten by birds, into *Cotylurus cornutus* and *Apatemon gracilis*. Other cysts which occur in *Erpobdella* clearly show a ring of hooks characteristic of cestodes. One such cyst has been shown to be the cysticercoid of *Hymenolepis parvula*, a small cestode found in the intestine of ducks.

Fig. 88. The life cycle of *Haemogregarina stepanowi*. *a–h*, from the turtle *Emys orbicularis; i–n*, from the leech *Placobdella costata; a*, schizont with fully formed merozoites, from bone marrow; *b*, entry of merozoite into blood corpuscle; *c, d, e*, further merozoite formation; *f*, formation of gamonts; h_1, macrogametocyte; h_2, microgametocyte; *i*, maturing of macrogametes; *k*, fusion of gametes; *l*, oocyst; *m*, sporozoite formation; *n*, free sporozoite in proboscis blood vessel of leech. From Herter, 1937, after Reichenow.

The existence of parasites with this type of life history provides evidence that water birds and fish are predators of leeches. Other evidence is scanty since leeches seldom leave indigestible remains so that they may be identified from stomach contents. From direct observation of the feeding habits of various water birds and fish and from occasional records from stomachs it is possible to say that erpobdellids in particular are preyed upon by herons, swans,

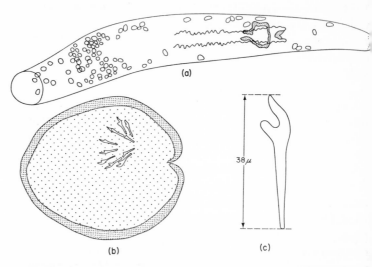

FIG. 89.   (a) diagram showing cysticercoid stages of the cestode *Hymenolepis parvula* distributed in the tissues of a specimen of the leech *Erpobdella octoculata* (drawn from a whole mount); (b) a drawing of one cysticercoid, showing the ten characteristic hooks;   (c) details of one hook.   Original.

ducks, bitterns, trout, perch, tench, sticklebacks and eels. There is no reason to suppose that they are rejected by aquatic amphibia and mammals, and are no doubt taken by carnivorous inverte-brates such as Hemiptera and Odonata. The mortality rates in natural populations of *Erpobdella octoculata*, *Glossiphonia compla-nata* and *Helobdella stagnalis* have been roughly estimated for certain habitats in Britain (Mann, 1953b, 1957a, b). In each case there was a heavy mortality in the first three months of life, more than 95% of the offspring being lost. In *Erpobdella* and *Glossiphonia*, where most individuals lived for 2 years, there was subsequently a mortality at the rate of one third to two thirds of the population per annum (Table 10). In *Helobdella*, where there are

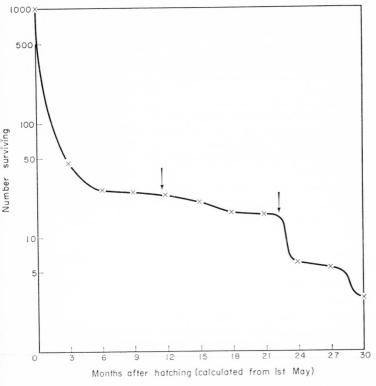

Fig. 90. Survival curve for 1000 newly hatched young of *Glossiphonia complanata*. From Mann, 1957.

two generations a year, the rate of mortality is correspondingly higher.

Looking over our very incomplete knowledge of the ecology of leeches, it appears that for the blood-sucking ectoparasites the most important single factor influencing distribution and abundance is the presence or absence of an appropriate host organism. In temperate climates, however, the predatory macrophagous

TABLE 10. COMPARISON OF THE LIFE HISTORIES OF
Glossiphonia complanata AND *Erpobdella octoculata*

	Glossiphonia complanata	Erpobdella octoculata
Breeding period	March–May	June–Aug.
Average number of young per parent	26	23·5
Mortality in the first 6–9 months of life	97%	91%
Proportion of year-group breeding at 1 year old	70% or less	87%
Mortality from 6 to 18 months	33%	49%
Proportion of year group breeding at 2 years old	100%	100%
Mortality from 18 to 30 months	84–88%	69%
Proportion of total population surviving to 3 years	5–6%	4%

forms greatly outnumber the sanguivorous parasites and these tend to feed on a wider variety of animals, so that almost any aquatic habitat will contain some suitable food organisms. For these the chemical and physical characters of the environment sway the balance in their competition with other organisms, the oxygen and calcium content of the water and the rate of water movement being particularly important.

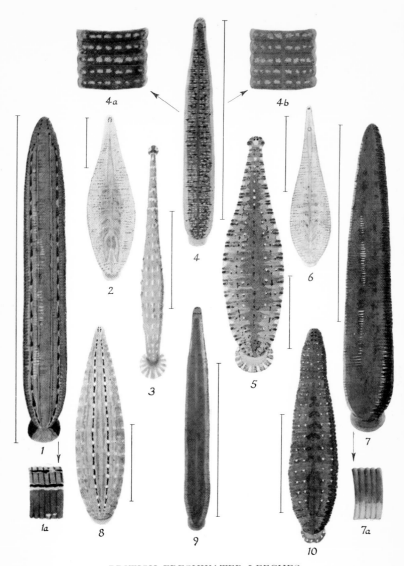

BRITISH FRESHWATER LEECHES

1. *Hirudo medicinalis.* 1a, a few annuli in lateral view. 2. *Glossiphonia heteroclita.* 3. *Piscicola geometra.* 4. *Erpobdella octoculata.* 4a and 4b, a few annuli in dorsal view, enlarged to show variation in the amount of black pigment present. 5. *Hemiclepsis marginata.* 6. *Helobdella stagnalis.* 7. *Haemopis sanguisuga.* 7a, a few annuli in lateral view. 8. *Glossiphonia complanata.* 9. *Erpobdella testacea.* 10. *Theromyzon tessulatum.*

The vertical line beside each leech represents its actual length.

From a water-colour painting made by Dr. E. V. Watson. Reproduced from Scientific Publication No. 14 of the Freshwater Biological Association, by kind permission of the Council.

APPENDIX A

THE SYSTEMATICS OF FRESHWATER
AND TERRESTRIAL LEECHES

By K. H. MANN

To give a full and accurate account of the leeches of the world as
far as they are known is beyond the scope of this book, even if it
were not an impossible task on account of the number of genera
and species that have been named without providing an adequate
description. To assess the validity of these names and the proper
relationships of the leeches which bear them would require many
years of work in many parts of the world.

This appendix and the one following are attempts to present a
summary of the present position as far as it can be gleaned from
the literature without study of the original specimens. Nearly
three quarters of the world's genera are found in fresh water or
terrestrial habitats and these form the subject of Appendix A. The
genera are reviewed, with indications of their geographical distribution, and a key is given for the identification to species of the
freshwater leeches of Central Europe, Britain and North America.

The marine genera have been treated separately by Professor
E. W. Knight-Jones in Appendix B. He has given a key to the genera
of the world and followed this with an account of the main characters
of each genus and of the species occurring in the North Atlantic.

Synopsis of the Hirudinea

Order Hirudinea
    Suborder ACANTHOBDELLAE
        Family ACANTHOBDELLIDAE
            one Genus *Acanthobdella* Grube 1850
A parasite of salmonid fishes of Lake Baikal and other parts of
Russia and Finland.

Suborder RHYNCHOBDELLAE

Family GLOSSIPHONIIDAE Vaillant 1890

Autrum (1939) divided the family into the subfamilies *Glossiphoniinae* in which the mouth is within the cup of the anterior sucker and the *Haementeriinae* in which the mouth is a small pore on the rim of the anterior sucker. Since 1939 several genera have been set up with insufficient description for a decision to be made as to which subfamily should hold them. Caballero (1956) and Moore (1959) amended the scheme in various ways and the arrangement given below is an attempt to incorporate the valid points of each scheme.

Subfamily *Glossiphoniinae* Autrum 1939

Genera: *Glossiphonia* Johnson 1816, a world-wide freshwater genus comprising mainly mollusc feeders which roll into a ball when handled; *Batracobdella* Viguier 1879, resembling *Glossiphonia* in appearance and habits but differing in internal anatomy; world-wide distribution; *Helobdella* Blanchard 1876, also world-wide with many species; small, attacking mainly freshwater invertebrates; *Theromyzon* Filippi 1867, a parasite of buccal and nasal cavities of water fowl; cosmopolitan; *Hemiclepsis* Vedjowsky 1883, sometimes grouped with *Theromyzon;* sucks blood of fish and amphibians; Europe and Asia; *Ancyrobdella* Oka 1917, Japan; *Oligoclepsis* Oka 1935, Japan; *Marsupiobdella* Goddard and Malan 1912, parasite of African freshwater crabs; has an internal brood pouch opening ventrally.

Subfamily HAEMENTERIINAE Autrum 1939

Genera: *Haementeria* Philippi 1849, many S. American species, including *H. officinalis* the medicinal leech of Mexico; *Placobdella* Blanchard 1893, of S. Europe, America, Asia and Africa; sometimes made a subgenus of *Haementeria;* includes parasites of man, other mammals and reptiles; *Paraclepsis* Harding 1924, India, and *Parabdella* Autrum 1936, India and Ceylon, Africa and N. America are often also united under *Haementeria* or *Placobdella; Oculobdella* Autrum 1936, N. and S. America; *Anoculobdella* Weber 1915, S. America; *Granelia* Harant and Vernières 1935, Central Africa; *Desmobdella* Oka 1930, S. America; *Oligobdella* Moore, 1918, N. and S. America, Japan, Korea and New Zealand; attacks

Amphibia; *Torix* R. Blanchard 1893, of China should perhaps be united with *Oligobdella; Actinobdella* Moore 1901, of N. America, sucks blood of vertebrates.

Genera of Uncertain Subfamily

Archaeobdella Grimm 1876	*Dartevellida* Sciacchitano 1939
Dermobdella Philippi 1867	*Dundjibdella* Sciacchitano 1939
Lobina Moquin-Tandon 1846	*Matadibdella* Sciacchitano 1939
Semilageneta Goddard 1908	*Trigonobdella* Sciacchitano 1939.

Family PISCICOLIDAE Johnston 1865
(= Ichthyobdellidae Apathy 1888)

The majority of the members of this family are marine leeches but a few are found in fresh water. The marine forms are reviewed separately in Appendix B.

Freshwater genera: *Piscicola* Blainville 1818, a fish parasite, in all parts of the world except Australasia and Polynesia; *Cystobranchus* Diesing 1859, also a fish parasite, S. Europe, Asia, N. America, Mexico; *Ozobranchus* Quatrefages 1832, attacks tortoises, crocodiles and pelicans of Africa, S. America, Asia; *Phyllobdella* Moore, 1939, Africa, on *Barbus; Illinobdella* Meyer 1940, fish parasite of Alaska; *Piscicolaria* Whitman 1889, N. America.

Suborder GNATHOBDELLAE
Family HIRUDIDAE

In this family are many important blood-sucking parasites of man and domestic animals:

Hirudo Linnaeus 1758, Europe, Asia, Africa, introduced into N. America; used in medicine; *Limnatis* Moquin-Tandon 1827, enters the nostrils of horses and men when drinking, S. Europe, Africa, Asia; *Poecilobdella* Blanchard 1893 (=*Hirudinaria* Whitman 1886 preoccupied) cattle leech of India and S.E. Asia; *Dinobdella* Moore 1927, enters the air passages of mammals, may remain for very long periods; India, Burma, Ceylon; *Hirudobdella* Goddard 1910, Australasia; *Macrobdella* Verrill 1872, important mammalian parasite of N. America; *Oxyptychus* Grube 1850 occupies the same niche in S. America; *Aetheobdella* Moore 1935, New South Wales; *Limnobdella* Blanchard 1893, Australia and New Zealand.

There is a tendency in some genera for the jaws to be reduced and the leech to become macrophagous:
Haemopis Savigny 1820, widespread in the N. Hemisphere; *Philobdella* Verrill 1874, N. America; *Myxobdella* Oka 1917, India, China, Africa; *Whitmania* Blanchard 1887, India, China, Japan; *Americobdella* Caballero 1956 (=*Cardea* Blanchard 1917 pre occupied) is an aberrant burrowing form from S. America, placed by some authorities in a separate family.

Other genera include: *Democedes* Kinberg 1866; *Hararbdella* Sciacchitano 1941; *Hexabdella* Verril 1872; *Hylacobdella* Sciacchitano 1935; *Mongbwalubdella* Sciacchitano 1939; *Paraobdella* Blanchard 1896; *Pintobdella* Caballero 1937; *Praobdella* Blanchard 1896; *Typhlobdella* Diesing 1850.

Family HAEMADIPSIDAE Blanchard 1893

In this family we have the sanguivorous land leeches found most abundantly in S.E. Asia and Indonesia.

Genera: *Haemadipsa* Tennent 1861; S.E. Asia from India to China, Japan, Philippines, Borneo, New Guinea, Madagascar, Seychelles; *Mesobdella* Blanchard 1893, Chili; *Nesophilaemon* Nybelin 1943, Juan Fernandez; *Phytobdella* Blanchard 1894, Philippines, New Guinea, Malaya; *Planobdella* Blanchard 1894, Borneo, Celebes; *Tritetrabdella* Moore, 1938, Malaya.

The following genera are distinguished by the loss of the median dorsal jaw: *Philaemon* Blanchard 1897, Madagascar, Australia, Samoa, S. America, Juan Fernandez; *Chtonobdella* Grube 1866, Australia and New Guinea; *Idiobdella* Harding 1913, Seychelles.

Xerobdella Frauenfeld 1868 from Yugoslavia and *Diestecostoma* Vaillant 1890 from Mexico and Guatemala are land leeches of aberrant form. Ringuelet (1954) separated them into a new family Xerobdellidae.

Family SEMISCOLECIDAE Scriban and Autrum 1934

Central and South American amphibious leeches, related to the Hirudidae, in which the jaws are reduced to a single median dorsal rudiment, the crop has only rudimentary caeca and there is usually more than one pair of testes per segment.

Genera: *Semiscolex* Kinberg 1866; *Semiscolecides* Augener 1930; *Orchibdella* Ringuelet 1945; *Potamobdella* Caballero 1931.

Suborder PHARYNGOBDELLAE
Family ERPOBDELLIDAE

These are the leeches with the most extreme modifications for a predaceous life. Some are aquatic, devouring freshwater invertebrates, while others take up a burrowing existence at the edges of lakes or streams, or occasionally become fully terrestrial, devouring earthworms.

Genera: *Erpobdella* Blainville 1818, widespread in the northern hemisphere; *Dina* E. Blanchard 1892, with a similar distribution, is sometimes regarded as a subgenus of *Erpobdella; Trocheta* Dutrochet 1817, Europe and Asia; *Salifa* Blanchard 1897, Africa, Asia; *Barbronia* Johansson 1918, Africa, India, Malaya, Indonesia; *Odontobdella* Oka 1923, China, Japan, Formosa; *Orobdella* Oka 1895, Japan; *Mimobdella* Blanchard 1897, Sumatra, Borneo; *Dineta* Goddard 1909, Australia; *Ornithobdella* Benham 1909, New Zealand; *Nephelopsis* Verrill 1872, N. America. There is a group of S. American genera: *Bibula* Blanchard 1917; *Cylicobdella* Grube 1871; *Hypsobdella* Weber 1913; *Lumbricobdella* Kennel 1886.

Family TREMATOBDELLIDAE Johansson 1913

Leeches closely resembling the Erpobdellidae but having a pore from the gut to the body wall (on segment XIII), either mid-dorsally or mid-ventrally.

Genera: *Trematobdella* Johansson 1913, Africa; *Acrabdella* Harding 1931, Sumatra; *Foraminobdella* Kaburaki 1921, India; *Gastrostomobdella* Moore 1929, Malaya, Sarawak, Borneo, Hawaii.

The Collection, Preservation and Identification of Leeches

Most leeches avoid light and should be looked for under stones or in the crevices of aquatic plants. Blood sucking ectoparasites are sometimes collected with their hosts, but most freshwater species drop off after taking a meal.

The identification of leeches is rendered difficult or even impossible by unsuitable preservation. If dropped alive into preservatives such as 70% alcohol or 4% formaldehyde they contract strongly and such features as the eyes and the genital pores are difficult to discern. They should therefore be narcotized

in weak alcohol, chloroform, chloretone, magnesium sulphate or
soda water. Excessive relaxation leads to the annuli being difficult
to make out and practice is needed before the right degree of
narcotization is achieved. The method favoured by the author is
to add 70% alcohol to the water containing living leeches, gradually increasing the concentration over a period of about 30 min
until movement ceases. The leeches are then removed, passed
rapidly between the fingers to straighten them and remove excess
mucus, and then laid out and kept flat while the fixative is poured
on. Alcohol or formaldehyde is suitable for simple morphological
work, but Bouin's or Flemming's fixative should be used for
histological studies.

The characters which are fundamental in leech identification
are the annulation, the number and arrangement of eyes and the
positions of the male and female genital pores. To determine the
number of annuli per segment look for segmentally repeated
features such as colour pattern and sensillae (see Chapter 2). To
see the eyes, flatten the head of a narcotized leech between two
glass slides. If the leech has been fixed and the eyes are hidden
by pigment, decolorize the head by immersion in 5% caustic
potash. The genital pores are in the mid-ventral line about one-
third of the distance from anterior to posterior suckers. The male
pore is normally anterior and the more prominent. The female
pore is often small and difficult to see. It is seen most easily
immediately after narcotization, its position often being revealed
by some colour difference which is lost during fixation.

A KEY TO THE FRESHWATER LEECHES OF CENTRAL EUROPE,
THE BRITISH ISLES, AND NORTH AMERICA NORTH OF THE
RIO GRANDE

The species to which this key refers are those included in the
following works:

AUTRUM, H. 1958. *Die Tierwelt Mitteleuropas*. I, 7b. *Hirudinea*.
MANN, K. H. 1954. A key to the British Freshwater Leeches, with
    Notes on their Ecology. *Freshwater Biological Association
    Scientific Publication* 14.

MOORE, J. P. 1959. *Hirudinea* in *Freshwater Biology* (2nd ed.)
  Edited by W. T. EDMONDSON.

MEYER, M. C. and MOORE, J. P. 1954. Notes on Canadian Leeches
  (Hirudinea) with the Description of a New Species. *Wassman.
  J. Biol.* **12**, 63–96.

References to full descriptions will be found in these.

As the various geographical areas have many species in common
a combined key to the freshwater species has been produced.

SECTION 1.   KEY TO FAMILIES

1.   Mouth a small pore on the oral sucker from which a
      proboscis may be protruded; no jaws present; blood
      colourless.

                    Suborder Rhynchobdellae   3

—   Mouth large, occupying entire cavity of the oral
      sucker; no proboscis; blood red   2

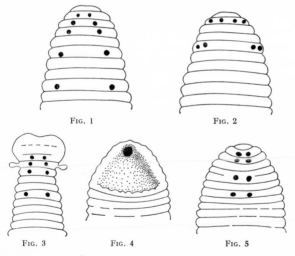

FIG. 1   FIG. 2

FIG. 3   FIG. 4   FIG. 5

FIG. 1–3 and 5.   Dorsal views of the heads of various leeches
to illustrate the arrangement of the eyes: 1, a gnathobdellid;
2, a pharyngobdellid; 3, *Xerobdella;* 5, *Theromyzon.*

FIG. 4.   Ventral view of the head of *Placobdella* to show mouth
on rim of anterior sucker.

2. Eyes, 5 pairs forming lateral crescents as in Fig. 1; 5 annuli per segment in the mid body region; pharynx short, less than quarter-length of body; mouth armed with toothed jaws; testes in large sacs arranged segmentally in pairs.

Suborder Gnathobdellae 4

— Eyes, 3 or 4 pairs arranged in two transverse rows as in Fig. 2; 5 annuli per segment or number increased by sub-division of annuli; pharynx long, about one-third length of body; mouth with muscular ridges but no jaws; testes in small, numerous bunched sacs.

Suborder Pharyngobdellae
Family ERPOBDELLIDAE 53

3. Body at rest depressed, not divided into distinct anterior and posterior regions; head usually much narrower than the body with anterior sucker not, or only slightly distinct from the body; usually 3 annuli per segment in the mid body region; eyes confined to the head except in *Placobdella hollensis*.

Family GLOSSIPHONIIDAE 5

— Body at rest cylindrical and (especially when contracted) usually divided at segment XIII into distinct anterior and posterior regions; head sucker usually distinctly marked off from the body; usually more than 3 annuli per segment; simple eyes may be present on head, neck and posterior sucker.

Family PISCICOLIDAE (=ICHTHYOBDELLIDAE) .. 31

4. Eyes, 5 pairs, the third and fourth separated by 1 annulus (Fig. 1).

Family HIRUDIDAE 40

— Eyes, 4 pairs, the third and fourth separated by 2 annuli (Fig. 3).

Family HAEMADIPSIDAE 52

SECTION 2. KEY TO THE FAMILY GLOSSIPHONIIDAE

5. Mouth within the anterior sucker cavity, on segments

II–IV; body only moderately flattened; salivary glands
diffuse; no oesophageal pouches   6
— Mouth on anterior rim of sucker (Fig. 4) body often
excessively flattened; salivary glands usually compact;
oesophageal pouches often present   20

6. Eyes, 4 pairs arranged as in Fig. 5; body (except when
distended with eggs) soft and translucent; small,
hungry leeches strap shaped with dilated head, but
mature recently fed leeches almost globular.

Theromyzon Philippi 1884   7

— Eyes fewer than 4 pairs; body usually opaque and firm   10

7. Gonopores separated by 2 annuli   8

— Gonopores separated by more than 2 annuli   9

8. From Central Europe.

Theromyzon maculosum (Rathke 1862).

— From North America.

Theromyzon meyeri (Livanow 1902).

9. Gonopores separated by 3 annuli.

Theromyzon rude (Baird 1863).

— Gonopores separated by 4 annuli.

Theromyzon tessulatum (O. F. Müller 1774).

10. Head and anterior sucker when at rest rather broader
than the body segments just behind them (Fig. 6);
eyes, 2 pairs on annuli 3–5; colour green or pale yellow
with 7 longitudinal rows of lemon yellow spots; size
at rest about 17 × 5 mm.

Hemiclepsis marginata (O. F. Müller 1774)

— Head and anterior sucker not wider than the body
segments just behind (Fig. 7); eyes not arranged as
in Fig. 6   11

11. Eyes, 1 pair, simple, well separated; small leeches at rest
about 10 mm long.   *Helobdella* E. Blanchard   12

— Eyes more than 1 pair, or if 1 pair these are lobed
showing that they have been formed by the fusion of
several eyes (Fig. 8)   15

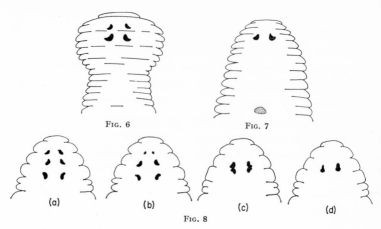

FIG. 6   FIG. 7

(a)   (b)   (c)   (d)

FIG. 8

FIG. 6–8. Dorsal views of the heads of various leeches to illustrate eye arrangement: 6, *Hemiclepsis*, 7, *Helobdella* showing chitinous scute; 8(a)–(d) variations in the eyes of *Glossiphonia complanata*.

12. A horny scute present dorsally about one-sixth of the distance from the anterior to the posterior sucker.

H. stagnalis (L.)

— No dorsal scute present   13

13. Body cylindrical, very slender, translucent, colourless; only one pair of crop caeca. *H. elongata* (Castle 1899)

— Body moderately flattened, wider posteriorly; normally 6 pairs of crop caeca but some may collapse when empty   14

14. Tubercles absent or limited to mid-dorsal line of posterior segments; colour coffee brown with 6 or 7 white spots on every third annulus.

H. fusca (Castle 1900)

— Tubercles absent or nearly so; with prominent longitudinal brown stripes and transverse rows of white spots.   *H. punctata-lineata* Moore 1939.

— Tubercles small, smooth and conical, deeply pigmented and often double; many fine longitudinal light and dark lines, no large white spots.   *H. lineata* (Verrill, 1874)

[*G. fusca* (Castle) part]

— Tubercles prominent, numerous (5–9 longitudinal rows), smooth, conical, black or dark brown; general colour dark yellowish brown.   *H. papillata* Moore 1906
[*G. fusca* (Castle) part]

15. Body of firm consistency; crop with 6 pairs of lateral diverticula (the anterior ones may collapse when empty); eyes normally 3 pairs but some fusion may take place.   *Glossiphonia* Johnson 1816   16

— Body of soft consistency; crop with 7 pairs of lateral diverticula; eyes, 3, 2 or 1 pairs.
Batracobdella Viguier 1879   17

16. Adults at rest more than 15 mm long; prominent dorsal tubercles usually present; eyes in 2 longitudinal rows but variable in number and extent of fusion (Fig. 8); gonopores separated by 2 annuli; 10 pairs of testes; patterned with brown, yellow or green.
Glossiphonia complanata (L.)

FIG. 9.   Head of *Glossiphonia heteroclita*.

— Adults at rest less than 15 mm long; no dorsal tubercles; first pair of eyes closer together than the others (Fig. 9); gonopores united; 6 pairs of testes; colour uniform amber or whitish with median dorsal brown pigment.
Glossiphonia heteroclita (L.)

17. European species   18
— American species   19

18. Large and distinct tubercles present dorsally (Fig. 10);

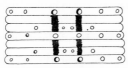

FIG. 10.   Part of the dorsal surface of *Batracobdella verrucata* showing tubercles.

at the level of the genital pores, but on the dorsal surface, 2 large irregular blotches of colour; eyes, 3 pairs, in two close parallel rows, often with the first pair smaller than the others or almost touching in the mid-dorsal line; colour, dark green, spotted with yellow, with 2 longitudinal regularly interrupted dark lines dorsally; about 25 mm × 10 mm.

Batracobdella verrucata (Fr. Müller 1884)

— No conspicuous tubercles or dorsal blotches; eyes, 2 pairs, often fused in various ways; colour similar to above species; smaller, about 10 mm × 4 mm.

Batracobdella paludosa (Carena 1824)

19. Eyes, 2 pairs, first pair close together or fused.

Batracobdella paludosa (Carena 1824)

— Eyes, 1 pair, close together or fused; no white bar on segment VI.   Batracobdella picta (Verrill 1872)

— Eyes, 1 pair, usually fused, surrounded by a white area; a dense white bar on segment VI.

Batracobdella phalera Graf 1899

20. Mid-body segments with 3 annuli of which the first and third may be faintly subdivided; body at rest very broad and flat; salivary glands compact; epididymis a tight mass.   Placobdella Blanchard 1896   21

— Mid-body segments with 2–6 annuli; body at rest less broad and flat; salivary glands diffuse; epididymis loosely coiled   28

21. European species.
Placobdella [= Haementeria] costata (Fr. Müller 1846)

— American species   22

22. Head distinctly wider than the segments just behind it; 3 prominent dorsal ridges bearing tubercles; eyes clearly separated.   Placobdella montifera Moore 1912.

— Without widened head and dorsal ridges   23

23. Anus separated from posterior sucker by a slender, tapering peduncle comprising about 16 annuli.

Placobdella pediculata Heminway 1912

— Anus close to posterior sucker, no peduncle 25

25. Minute simple supplementary eyes near mid-dorsal line of head; every third annulus deeply pigmented green and brown; length 25–40 mm
Placobdella hollensis (Whitman 1872)

— No supplementary eyes; length 50–100 mm; very flat 26

26. Dorsal tubercles inconspicuous or absent; brown, green and yellow pigment dorsally, about 12 bluish stripes ventrally. *Placobdella parasitica* (Say 1824)

— Dorsal tubercles prominent 27

27. With large, rough dorsal tubercles and many smaller ones; body translucent; colouring a fine mixture.
Placobdella ornata (Verrill 1872)
[=*P. rugosa* (Verrill)]

— With smaller, more uniform tubercles; colour, mottled on surface, about 30 dark brown lines beneath and these remain after preservation.
Placobdella multilineata Moore 1953

— With small but conspicuous tubercles in 5 longitudinal rows, appearing as whitish spots on coffee brown stripes; ground colour pale, brownish, with white or yellow spots. *Placobdella papillifera* (Verrill 1872)

28. 2 annuli per segment; 7 pairs of crop caeca; 5 pairs of testis sacs. *Oligobdella* Moore 1918
Oligobdella biannulata (Moore 1900)

— More than 2 annuli per segment 29

29. Posterior sucker with marginal circle of glands and retractile papillae. *Actinobdella* Moore 1901 30

— Posterior sucker without marginal retractile papillae; 3 annuli per segment; gonopores united; 5 or 6 pairs of crop caeca. *Oculobdella* Autrum 1936
Oculobdella lucida Meyer and Moore 1954

30. 3 annuli per segment; about 30 conical papillae on posterior sucker; dorsal tubercles prominent, in 5 longitudinal rows.
Actinobdella triannulata Moore 1924.

— 6 equal annuli per segment; about 60 sucker papillae; dorsal tubercles in 5 longitudinal rows.

Actinobdella annectens Moore 1906

— 6 unequal annuli per segment; about 30 sucker papillae; tubercles confined to mid-dorsal row.

Actinobdella inequiannulata Moore 1901

SECTION 3.   KEY TO THE FAMILY PISCICOLIDAE

31.   Pulsatile vesicles on margins of body (Fig. 11) 32

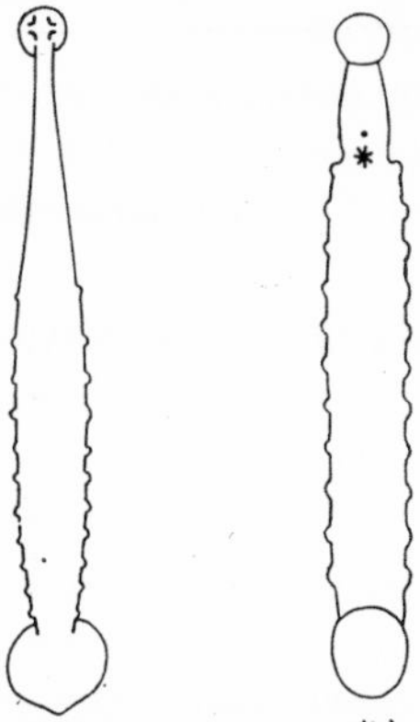

FIG. 11.   Outlines of (a) *Piscicola geometra* and (b) *Cystobranchus fasciatus* showing lateral pulsatile vesicles.

— Pulsatile vesicles absent 38
32.   Pulsatile vesicles small, difficult to see on preserved leeches; 14 annuli per segment; body not clearly divided into anterior and posterior regions.

Piscicola Blainville 1818   33

— Pulsatile vesicles large, clearly seen after preservation; 7 annuli per segment; body clearly divided into anterior and posterior regions.   *Cystobranchus* Diesing 1859   35
33.   Ocelli present on posterior sucker.. 34
— Ocelli absent from posterior sucker; eyes, 2 (or 1) pairs; gonopores separated by 3 annuli.

Piscicola punctata (Verrill 1871)

34.   8–10 crescent-shaped ocelli on posterior sucker; gono-
      pores separated by 2 annuli; sperm duct convoluted.
                              Piscicola salmositica Meyer 1946

—   10–12 punctiform ocelli on posterior sucker; 2 annuli
      between gonopores; sperm duct simply looped.
                              Piscicola milneri (Verrill 1871)

—   12–14 punctiform ocelli on posterior sucker; 3 annuli
      between gonopores; sperm duct simply looped.
                              Piscicola geometra (L.)

35.   American species.   *Cystobranchus verrilli* Meyer 1940
—   European species   36
36.   Eyes absent from anterior and posterior suckers; no
      distinct copulatory area.
                              Cystobranchus mammillatus (Malm 1863)

—   4 eyes on anterior sucker and 10 ocelli on posterior
      sucker; a well marked copulatory area (Fig. 12)   37

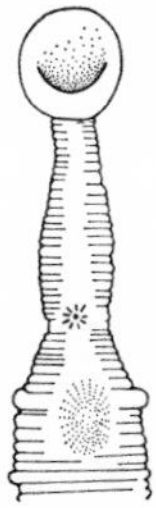

Fig. 12.   Anterior portion of *Cystobranchus fasciatus*, ventral
view, to show copulatory area (shaded).   After Autrum.

37.   Diameter of anterior sucker nearly twice the greatest
      width of anterior body region.
                              Cystobranchus fasciatus (Kollar 1842)

—   Diameter of anterior sucker about the same as the
      greatest width of the anterior body region.
                              Cystobranchus respirans (Troschel 1859)

38.   3 annuli per segment; no clear division between
      anterior and posterior body regions.
                              Piscicolaria Whitman 1889
                         One species, *P. reducta* Meyer 1940

—   14 annuli per segment; contracted specimens reveal distinction between anterior and posterior body regions.
                                   Illinobdella Meyer 1940   39

39.   Gonopores separated by 8 annuli (apparently 4 annuli faintly subdivided); distinct seminal vesicle present.
                              Illinobdella moorei Meyer 1940

—   Gonopores separated by 4 annuli (2 faintly subdivided); no seminal vesicle.   *Illinobdella alba* Meyer 1940

SECTION 4.   KEY TO THE FAMILY HIRUDIDAE

40.   Jaws well developed, with 1 row of sharp teeth; pharynx short and very muscular; crop with many large, lobed caeca   41

—   Jaws reduced, with 2 rows of blunt teeth; pharynx longer and less muscular; crop of adults with only the posterior pair of caeca well developed   45

41.   Copulatory glands present behind gonopores (Fig. 13).
                                   Macrobdella Verrill 1872   43

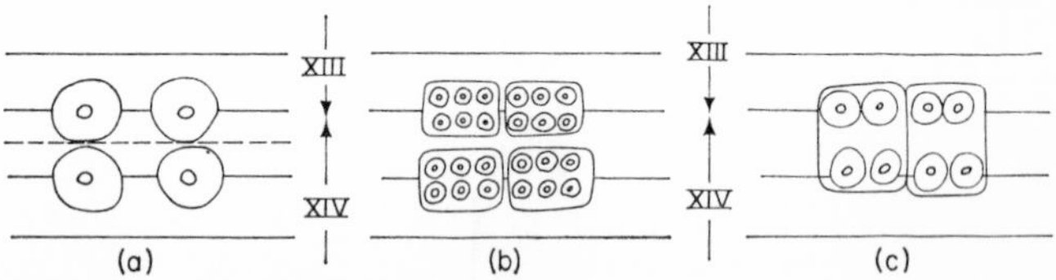

FIG. 13.   Diagrams of the arrangement of copulatory gland pores of *Macrobdella;* (a) *M. decora;* (b) *M. sestertia;* (c) *M. ditetra.* After Moore.

—   Copulatory glands absent   42

42.   Jaws with salivary gland papillae (Fig. 14); upper lip with median ventral groove (Fig. 15); diameter of caudal sucker about same as maximum width of body.
                                   Limnatis Moquin-Tandon
                        One species *L. nilotica* Savigny 1822

—   Jaws lacking salivary gland papillae; upper lip lacking median ventral groove; diameter of caudal sucker about $\frac{3}{4}$ maximum width of body.   *Hirudo* L.
                        One species *H. medicinalis* L.

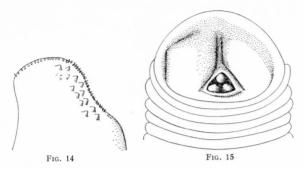

Fig. 14

Fig. 15

Fig. 14. Jaw of *Limnatis* to show salivary papillae.
After Autrum.

Fig. 15. Ventral view of anterior sucker of *Limnatis* showing
groove on ventral surface of upper lip and jaws protruding
through velar pore. After Autrum.

43. About 21 bright red spots in mid dorsal line.. .. .. **44**

— Red spots absent; 2 annuli between genital pores;
8 copulatory gland pores as in Fig. 13c; about 50 teeth
per jaw.   *Macrobdella ditetra* Moore 1953

44. 5 annuli between gonopores; 4 copulatory gland pores
as in Fig. 13a; about 65 teeth per jaw.
Macrobdella decora (Say 1824)

— $2\frac{1}{2}$ annuli between gonopores; 24 copulatory gland
pores as in Fig. 13b; about 40 teeth on each jaw.
Macrobdella sestertia Whitman 1884

45. 5 annuli between gonopores; copulatory glands absent;
jaws low and rounded, rarely absent; teeth large, blunt
and in 2 distinct rows.   *Haemopis* Savigny 1820 **46**

— 3 or 4 annuli between gonopores but in mature leeches
gonopores obscured by numerous gland pores (Fig. 16);
jaws high and narrow; teeth small and in rows which are
not entirely separated.   *Philobdella* Verrill 1874 **51**

46. European leech; segment VI with 3 annuli, VII with
4 annuli (Fig. 17a); colour varies from dark grey–green
to pale yellow-green, paler ventrally, with variable
amounts of black flecking; 11–19 pairs of teeth per jaw.
Haemopis sanguisuga (L.)

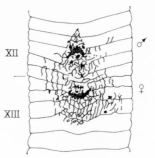

Fig. 16.   Ventral view of segments XII and XIII of *Philobdella gracilis* showing genital pores in glandular area.

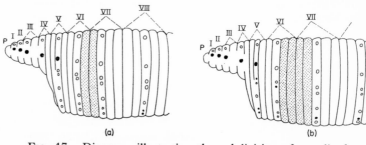

Fig. 17.   Diagrams illustrating the subdivision of annuli of segments VI and VII in certain species of *Haemopis*. The 2 annuli shaded in (a) are subdivided to form 4 annuli in (b). (*a*) *H. sanguisuga;* (*b*) *H. lateralis.*

48.   Colour variable but usually blotched with black, brown and yellowish grey; 12–16 pairs of teeth per jaw.
                              Haemopis marmorata (Say 1824)

—   With a median dorsal black stripe; 9–12 pairs of teeth per jaw.   *Haemopis kingi* Mather 1954

49.   Jaws present, bearing 20–25 teeth; dorsal surface usually with a median black stripe and orange marginal stripes.   *Haemopis lateralis* (Say 1824)

—   Jaws absent or vestigial; median dorsal stripe absent ..   50

50.   Genital pores in furrows between annuli; ground colour of ventral surface lighter than that of dorsal.
Haemopis grandis (Verrill 1874)

—   Genital pores in middle of annuli; ground colour of ventral surface not lighter, usually darker than that of dorsal.   *Haemopis plumbea* Moore 1912

51.   With a dark brown median dorsal stripe, no spots; about 20 teeth per jaw.
Philobdella floridana Verrill 1874

—   With a light yellow median dorsal stripe and dorso-lateral brown spots; about 40 teeth per jaw.
Philobdella gracilis Moore 1901

SECTION 5. KEY TO THE FAMILY HAEMADIPSIDAE

Only one genus in the area, *Xerobdella* v. Frauenfeld 1868 (Fig. 18).

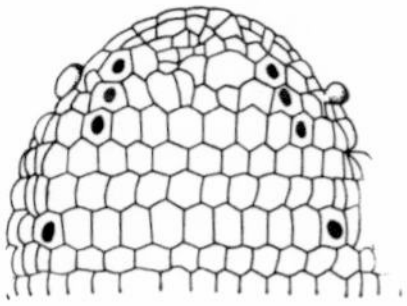

FIG. 18. Dorsal view of the head of *Xerobdella annulata*. From Autrum.

52.   3–3½ annuli between gonopores.
Xerobdella lecomtei v. Frauenfeld 1868

—   4½ annuli between gonopores.
Xerobdella annulata Autrum 1958

SECTION 6. KEY TO THE FAMILY ERPOBDELLIDAE

53.   European leeches (can be identified on external features)   54
—   American leeches (require dissection for further identification)   59
54.   All annuli of the body of about the same width   55

— In any group 6 consecutive annuli at least 1 is different from the rest, being either much narrower or wider and subdivided.. 56

55. Genital pores separated by 2–3½ annuli; typical forms with a broken network of black pigment on the dorsal surface.   *Erpobdella octoculata* L.

— Genital pores separated by 3½–5 annuli; typical forms lack black pigment dorsally, less common varieties may have a median dark line or a transparent body revealing deep lying black pigment.

                    Erpobdella testacea (Savigny 1820)

56. A group of 5 consecutive annuli consists of 4 of equal width and 1 which is wider but divided by a faint transverse furrow (Fig. 19); genital pores separated by 2–3 (or 3½) annuli.   *Dina* E. Blanchard 1892 57

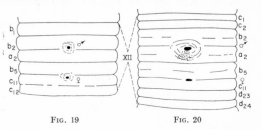

FIG. 19.   FIG. 20.

FIG. 19. Ventral view of segment XII of *Dina lineata* to show genital pores and annulation.

FIG. 20. Ventral view of segment XII of *Trocheta bykowskii* to show genital pores and annulation.

— The most common arrangement of annuli is 3 broad and 5 narrow (Fig. 20) but the narrow annuli may be associated in pairs forming broad annuli faintly subdivided or each broad annulus may be divided to form 2 narrow ones; there are many arrangements, all of which differ from those found in the other Erpobdellidae.

                    Trocheta Dutrochet 1817 58

57. Eyes present, number and position variable.

                    Dina lineata (O. F. Muller 1774)

—   Eyes absent.   *Dina absoloni* (Johansson 1913)

58.   Gonopores separated by 4½–10 annuli depending on the degree of subdivision of the annuli.

                Trocheta subviridis Dutrochet 1817

—   Gonopores separated by 2–4 annuli.

                Trocheta bykowskii Gedroyc 1913

59.   Vas deferens with a pre-atrial loop reaching to ganglion XI (Fig. 21)   61

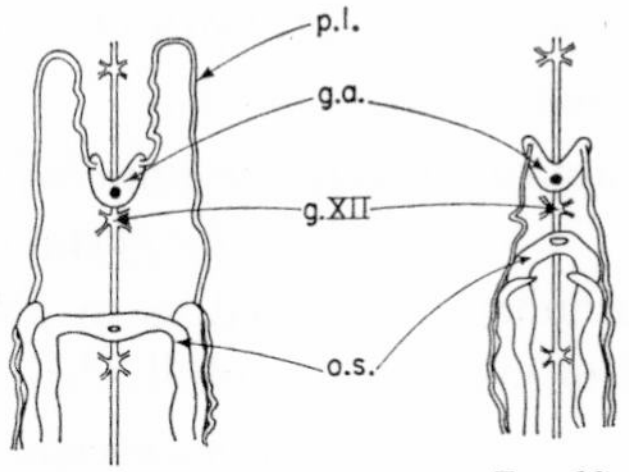

FIG. 21   FIG. 22

FIG. 21 and 22.   Dissection of reproductive systems in region of genital pores, ventral view; 21, *Trocheta;* 22, *Mooreobdella*, after Moore. *g.a.*, genital atrium; g. XII, twelfth ganglion; *o.s.*, ovarian sac; *p.l.* preatrial loop of male duct.

—   Vas deferens without preatrial loop (Fig. 22); every fifth annulus subdivided as in 56 above.

                Mooreobdella Pawlowski 1955   60

60.   Atrium ellipsoidal, wider than long, with horns shorter than diameter of median atrium; 3 annuli between gonopores *Mooreobdella microstoma* (Moore 1901)

—   Atrium globular with prominent horns longer than its diameter; gonopores separated by 2 annuli and normally on the rings, not in the furrows; eyes 4 (or 3) pairs; length 5 cm.

                Mooreobdella fervida (Verrill 1874)

—   Atrium globular as above; gonopores separated by 2 annuli and lying in the furrows; eyes, 3 pairs; length 3 cm.   *Mooreobdella bucera* (Moore 1947)

Fig. 23.   Dorsal and lateral views of the male genital atrium
of *Nephelopsis obscura*, after Moore.

61.   Atrial cornua spirally coiled, like ram's horn (Fig. 23);
Nephelopsis Verrill 1872
One species *Nephelopsis obscura* Verrill 1872

—   Atrial cornua not spirally coiled   62

62.   All annuli of approximately the same width.
Erpobdella puctata (Leidy 1870)

—   Every fifth annulus subdivided as in 56 above (occasionally 2 out of every 5 are subdivided)   63

63.   Eyes absent.   *Dina anoculata* Moore 1898

—   Eyes present   64

64.   Eyes, 3 pairs; 2 annuli between gonopores.
Dina lateralis (Verrill 1871)

—   Eyes 4 pairs; 3–3½ annuli between gonopores   65

65.   Length about 2 cm; a few dark spots or no pigment.
Dina parva Moore 1912

—   Length about 4–5 cm; with a dark median stripe and
blotches.   *Dina dubia* Moore and Meyer 1951

THE SYSTEMATICS OF MARINE LEECHES

By Professor E. W. Knight-Jones
Department of Zoology, University College of Swansea

The marine leeches constitute the greater part of the family Piscicolidae. They are even less well known than the freshwater and terrestrial forms, and it is not unusual to find undescribed species. The last synopsis was that of Herter (1935) but new forms have been described since. In this appendix a tentative key to the marine genera of the world is followed by a list of genera in alphabetical order, giving their characters and most of their North Atlantic species.

Marine leeches can seldom be collected to order but are often found at sea or on dead fish and have to be fixed by whatever method happens to be available. The technique of study is rather different from that used with freshwater forms. Internal anatomy is important and this can be observed by clearing in cedar wood oil but better by sectioning. The intersegmental testes are a useful guide to the limits of segments and make it possible to determine the number of annuli per segment in a cleared specimen. Clearing also reveals eyes, which may otherwise not be visible after death. Good sections are obtained after narcotizing with menthol and fixing in sea water Bouin.

The following terms and abbreviations are used in the key and descriptions:

abdomen, body behind clitellum, often flattened dorso–ventrally;
annuli, number of annuli per mid-body segment, the convention 3 (6) meaning that each of three annuli is faintly divided into two;
coelom, refers to the coelom of the mid-body (testicular) region;
coelom typical, as in *Piscicola*, with dorsal, ventral, lateral and

169

transverse lacunae linked to a row of pulsatile vesicles on each side (Fig. 27, p. 53); *diverticula*, the elongated posterior pair of crop diverticula which may be more or less fused together; *eyes*, eyes on head; *ganglia*, number of ganglia in the ventral chain, not including the suboesophageal and caudal masses; *ocelli*, simple eyes on posterior sucker; *pulsatile vesicles*, externally visible respiratory vesicles like those found in *Piscicola* (Fig. 17, p. 28); *trachelosome*, anterior part of body including clitellum.

KEY TO THE GENERA OF THE WORLD

1. Body with many conspicuous branchiae or tubercles .. 2
— Body smooth or with a single fin or row of vesicles on each side 6
2. Body with lateral branchiae 3
— Body with numerous tubercles 4
3. Branchiae finger-shaped and branching
Ozobranchus (Fig. 19, p. 31)
— Branchiae leaf-shaped and unbranched
Branchellion (Fig. 18, p. 30)
4. One annulus of each somite bears large tubercles, most of the other annuli bear small tubercles; 4–6 very distinct annuli per somite 5
— All tubercles small and arranged longitudinally in 6 rows dorsally and in 6 rows or absent ventrally; 12–14 annuli per somite .. .. *Oxytonostoma*
5. Body rounded with regions ill-defined
Pontobdella (Fig. 19, p. 31)
— Body sharply divided into slender trachelosome and broad flattened abdomen .. .. *Pontobdellina*
6. Body with a flattened, fin-like expansion extending along each side.. 7
— Body without lateral fins 8
7. Fins confined to anterior 2/3 of body; genital ducts with a common opening .. .. .. *Pterobdella* (Fig. 19, p. 31)
— Fins extending whole length of body; separate genital openings .. .. *Pterobdellina*

8. Eyes 9 pairs; oral sucker bears small papillae; from Southern Ocean 9
—   Eyes 0–3 pairs; oral sucker generally without papillae 10
9. Body with narrow trachelosome and broad flattened abdomen .. .. *Trulliobdella*
—   Body not clearly divided into regions .. .. *Cryobdellina*
10. Mouth at about the centre of oral sucker 11
—   Mouth in anterior border of oral sucker 30
11. Posterior sucker small, little or no wider than the posterior end of the body 12
—   Posterior sucker considerably wider than the posterior end of the body 15
12. With a row of at least 8 pulsatile vesicles on each side of abdomen 16
—   Pulsatile vesicles absent or no more than three on each side 13
13. Anterior sucker relatively huge, nearly as wide as the short flattened abdomen .. .. *Ganymedebdella*
—   Both suckers very small 14
14. No eyes .. .. *Hemibdella*
—   Eyes 1 pair on about tenth annulus; suckers almost covered by annuli .. .. *Myzobdella*
15. With a row of pulsatile vesicles on each side.. 16
—   Pulsatile vesicles absent or indistinguishable 18
16. With about 8 pulsatile vesicles on each side .. *Cyrillobdella*
—   With 11–13 pulsatile vesicles on each side 17
17. Abdomen broad, somewhat flattened and very distinct from narrow trachelosome; suckers rather small, narrower than abdomen .. .. *Trachelobdella*
—   Abdomen more or less rounded and not very distinct from trachelosome; posterior sucker wider than body .. .. *Calliobdella**

*The New Zealand genus *Makarabdella*, Richardson 1959 (Trans. roy. Soc. N.Z. 87,283) resembles *Calliobdella* in having 3 (6) annuli per somite but differs in that the bursa lacks an accessory muscular organ. Possession of 7 (14) annuli per somite in a leech of this kind would indicate a marine species of *Piscicola* or *Cystobranchus*.

18.	Annuli 12–14 per mid-body somite	19
—	Annuli 2–6 per mid-body somite	23
19.	Eyes absent	20
—	Eyes 2 or 3 pairs	22
20.	Median spermatheca lying between ovaries; from California	*Marsipobdella*
—	Spermatheca absent	21
21.	Posterior crop diverticula absent; from New Zealand	*Bdellamaris*
—	Posterior crop diverticula fused, with 5 fenestra; coelomic system typical, but pulsatile vesicles are hidden in skin	*Johanssonia*
22.	Annuli 12 per somite; testes 5 pairs	*Crangonobdella*
—	Annuli 14 per somite; testes 6 pairs	*Carcinobdella*
23.	Annuli 2 per mid-body somite; with 2 pairs eyes, each made up of several black pigment spots	*Janusion*
—	Annuli 3 (6) per mid-body somite; if eyes are present, each is a simple, rounded or crescent-shaped spot of pigment	24
24.	Posterior sucker somewhat compressed laterally, typically folded round a fin-ray but also capable of adhering to flat surfaces	*Sanguinothus*
—	Posterior sucker more or less circular in outline	25
25.	Coelom fairly spacious, not divided into lacunae	*Arctobdella*
—	Coelom restricted to narrow lacunae	26
26.	Dorsal and ventral lacunae both communicating segmentally with a contractile lateral lacuna lying in the dermis on each side	*Austrobdella*
—	Ventral lacuna lacking segmental communications with other lacunae	27
27.	Dorsal lacuna communicating segmentally with lateral lacunae	28
—	Dorsal lacuna lacking segmental communications with other lacunae	29

28. Abdomen rounded and not very distinct from trachelo-
    some; skin opaque .. .. *Ottoniobdella*
—   Abdomen broad, flattened and distinct from trachelo-
    some; skin transparent .. .. *Oceanobdella*
29. Testes 4 pairs; posterior sucker tends to face postero-
    dorsally .. .. *Cryobdella*
—   Testes 5 pairs; posterior sucker faces postero-ventrally
                                              Platybdella
30. Annuli 14 per somite .. .. *Carcinobdella*
—   Annuli 16 per somite .. .. *Notostomobdella*

GENERA OF MARINE LEECHES
WITH SOME OF THE SPECIES FROM THE NORTH ATLANTIC
AND NEIGHBOURING SEAS

Particularly distinctive characters are given in italics. The
treatment is not exhaustive and only a selection of references is
cited. Species reliably recorded from Britain are marked by
asterisks.

ARCTOBDELLA de Silva and Kabata 1961. Oral sucker
small, eyes 0, posterior sucker discoid, abdomen flattened and
smooth, annuli 3(6) but obscure, *coelom fairly spacious and not
divided into lacunae, diverticula separate*, ganglia 18+1 fused
anteriorly, testes 4 pairs.
  Arctobdella branchiarum de Silva and Kabata. 10 mm long.
Gills of *Drepanopsetta platessoides*. Iceland.

AUSTROBDELLA Badham 1916 (Ingram, 1957). Suckers
discoid, eyes 0–1 pair, abdomen flattened, smooth and forming
"shoulders" behind clitellum which is not more constricted than
rest of trachelosome, annuli 3 (6), *a contractile lacuna in dermis
throughout length of abdomen on each side* and without separate
pulsatile vesicles or subdermal lateral lacunae but coelom otherwise fairly typical, ganglia 21, testes 5 pairs. Two spp. from
Australia and Tasmania.
  Austrobdella anoculata Moore (1940). 5 mm long. Greenland.

BDELLAMARIS Richardson 1953. Like *Calliobdella* or *Trachelobdella* except annuli 12, *diverticula absent*. One sp. from New Zealand.

BRANCHELLION Savigny 1822 (Harding, 1910; Sukatschoff, 1912; Ingram, 1957). Suckers large, eyes 0–3 pairs, posterior sucker containing many minute subsidiary suckers, constricted clitellum partly covered by preputial fold of abdomen, abdomen flattened with *31–33 pairs of lateral foliaceous branchiae* (3 per somite), annuli 3 (6), pulsatile vesicles 11 pairs, coelom typical, diverticula fused, testes 5–6 pairs. At least 6 spp. mostly on elasmobranchs.

*Branchellion borealis Leigh-Sharpe (1933). 30 mm long, 31 pairs branchiae, no eyes, 4 tubercles dorsally on each of 4 anterior somites of trachelosome. Dorsally on *Raja clavata*. English Channel.

Branchellion ravenelii (Girard) (Meyer, 1941). 15 mm long, 31 pairs branchiae, 1 pair branching eye-spots. Ventrally on *Dasyatis hastatus, Amphotistius sabinus, Aetobatus freminvillii*. Florida and Carolina.

Branchellion torpedinis Savigny. 50 mm long, 33 pairs branchiae. On *Rhinobatis thouin, Raja clavata, Torpedo, Trygon pastinaca, Labrus, Rhombus maximus*. Mediterranean, North Sea, Ireland, Senegal.

CALLIOBDELLA Beneden and Hesse 1863 (Johansson, 1896; Oka, 1910; Selensky, 1915; Leigh-Sharpe, 1914 and 1916). Suckers discoid, eyes 0–2 pairs, *posterior sucker broader than body*, *abdomen more or less rounded*, annuli 3 (6), *pulsatile vesicles 11–13 pairs*, coelom typical, diverticula more or less fused, testes 6 pairs, *rounded muscular organ connected with bursa*. Several spp.

*Calliobdella lophii Beneden and Hesse. 50 mm long, eyes 0, posterior sucker 3–4 × breadth of oral sucker, abdomen somewhat flattened and trachelosome well defined. On *Lophius piscatorius*. W. Europe.

*Calliobdella nodulifera (Malm). 30 mm long, eyes 0, posterior sucker 2 × breadth of oral sucker, abdomen rounded and trachelosome ill defined. Externally on a variety of fish, especially gadoids. W. Europe, Faroes, Iceland.

Calliobdella punctata Beneden and Hesse. 20 mm long, eyes

2 pairs. On *Cottus bubalis* and *Blennius pholis*. Common at Roscoff (Brumpt, 1900).

CARCINOBDELLA Oka 1910 (1927; 1933). Suckers discoid (type species has mouth situated as in *Notostomobdella* and clitellum swollen), eyes 0–3 pairs, abdomen rounded, annuli 14, diverticula fused, testes 6 pairs. Three spp. off Japan.

CRANGONOBDELLA Selensky 1914; 1915 (Borovitzkaia, 1949). Resembling *Platybdella* but with annuli 12 and copulatory zone with vector tissue. Several spp. from Russian seas.
Crangonobdella murmanica Selensky. 20 mm long, eyes 3 pairs. On *Sclerocrangon boreas*. White Sea, E. Greenland.

CRYOBDELLA Harding 1922 (Brinkmann, 1948). Like *Platybdella* (Moore, 1938) except posterior sucker has finely serrated margin and is often bent dorsally, testes 4 pairs. One sp. from Antarctic.

CRYOBDELLINA Brinkmann 1948. Like *Platybdella* but *eyes 9 pairs*, ganglia 18, testes 4 pairs. One sp. from Antarctic.

CYMATOBRANCHUS. The promised description (Selensky, 1931) appears to have been forestalled by the author's death. The species referred to seems never to have been adequately described.

CYRILLOBDELLA Leigh-Sharpe 1933. Like *Trachelobdella* but 8 pairs of pulsatile vesicles. Single specimen incompletely described.
Cyrillobdella alcibiades Leigh-Sharpe. 8 mm long. From *Sargus annularis*. Mediterranean.

GANYMEDEBDELLA Leigh-Sharpe 1915. *Anterior sucker huge*, eyes 0, posterior sucker small, abdomen flattened and very broad, annuli 1, pulsatile vesicles 3 pairs, diverticula separate, testes 6 pairs.
Ganymedebdella cratere Leigh-Sharpe. 8 mm long. From cloacal papilla of *Callionymus*. North of Scotland.

HEMIBDELLA Selensky 1931. *Suckers small*, eyes 0, abdomen rounded, annuli 12, coelom typical but without vesicles, diverticula fused, testes 5 pairs, copulatory zone.

Hemibdella soleae (Beneden and Hesse). 5–10 mm long. Attached to scales on pigmented side of *Solea vulgaris, Solea impar* and *Solea monochir.* W. Europe, Greenland and Mediterranean.

ICHTHYOBDELLA Blainville 1827. Not a defined genus today but one to which several smooth-skinned leeches without pulsatile vesicles have been referred provisionally (Oka, 1910, 1931; Ingram, 1957).

JANUSION Leigh-Sharpe 1933. Suckers cup-shaped, eyes 2 pairs *consisting of clusters of black spots,* abdomen flattened, clitellum narrow, annuli 2, imperfectly described.
    *Janusion scorpii (Malm). 15 mm long. On *Cottus scorpius.* Plymouth, U.K.

JOHANSSONIA Selensky 1914. Suckers discoid, eyes 0, abdomen rounded and ill defined, annuli 14 (16), coelom typical but *pulsatile vesicles small, embedded in skin* and indistinguishable after death except by sectioning, diverticula fused with 5 fenestrae, testes 5–6 pairs.
    Johanssonia kolaensis Selensky. 20 mm long, posterior sucker broader than abdomen. On *Anarrhichas lupus.* Arctic seas.
    Johanssonia pantopodum Selensky, 1914. 20 mm long, posterior sucker not as broad as abdomen. On *Nymphon strömii.* Arctic and perhaps W. Europe.

MARSIPOBDELLA Moore 1952. Suckers discoid, eyes 0, trachelosome somewhat constricted, annuli 12–14, diverticula fused with 5 fenestrae, testes 5 pairs, *median spermatheca lying between ovaries.* One sp. California.

MYSIDOBDELLA Selensky 1927. Eyes 0, annuli 13, coelom as in *Hemibdella,* diverticula fused with 5 fenestrae, copulatory area poorly defined with no conducting tissue.
    Mysidobdella oculata Selensky. Uniform olive green. On *Mysis oculata.* White Sea.

MYZOBDELLA Leidy 1851 (Moore, 1946). Like *Hemibdella* but eyes 1 pair, coelom reduced to ventral lacuna, testes 4–5 pairs. At least one fresh water species (Meyer and Moore, 1954).
    Myzobdella lugubris Leidy. On the crab *Callinectes sapidus* in brackish coastal waters. New Jersey to North Carolina.

NOTOBDELLA Benham 1909. Suckers discoid, eyes 1 pair, abdomen rounded but distinct from trachelosome. One imperfectly described sp. from Antarctic.

NOTOSTOMOBDELLA Moore and Meyer 1951 (=*Notostomum* Johansson 1898). Suckers equally large and cup-shaped, mouth in anterior edge of oral sucker, eyes 0, abdomen rounded and ill-defined, annuli 14–16, coelom reduced to dorsal and ventral lacunae, diverticula fused with 5 fenestrae, testes 6 pairs.

Notostomobdella laeve (Levinsen, 1882). 100–150 mm long. On *Hippoglossus pingvis*, *Somniosus microcephalus* and *Platysomatichtys hippoglossoides*. Greenland.

OCEANOBDELLA Caballero 1956 (=*Abranchus* Johansson, 1929). Anterior sucker very small, eyes 3 pairs, posterior sucker discoid and usually with ring of ocelli, skin transparent, *clitellum constricted, abdomen flattened*, annuli 3 (6), coelom somewhat reduced so that *segmental transverse communications link lateral and dorsal lacunae only*, diverticula separate or partially fused, testes 4–6 pairs.

Oceanobdella microstoma (Johansson, 1896). 25 mm long, unpigmented, ventrally on *Cottus scorpius*. W. Europe, Iceland, Greenland, Spitzbergen.

Oceanobdella blennii (Knight–Jones, 1940). 12 mm long, transversely banded with brown and capable of extreme abdominal flattening, posterior sucker less broad than abdomen and with few or no ocelli, attached behind pectoral fin of *Blennius pholis*. Anglesey and Swansea, U.K.

Oceanobdella sexoculata (Malm, 1863). 11 mm long, banded with brown, posterior sucker somewhat broader than abdomen and with complete ring of ocelli round margin. On *Zoarces viviparus, Gadus callarias, Cyclopterus lumpus*. W. Sweden.

OPHIBDELLA Beneden and Hesse 1863. Young of *Pontobdella* (Apàthy, 1888)?

OSTREOBDELLA Oka 1927. Suckers discoid and equally large, eyes 1 pair, abdomen rounded and ill-defined, annuli 14, internal anatomy undescribed. One sp. Japan.

OTTONIOBDELLA Moore and Meyer 1951 (= *Ottonia* Malm) (Johansson, 1929). Like *Oceanobdella* except anterior sucker discoid, skin opaque and pigmented, *abdomen rounded and ill defined.*

Ottoniobdella brunnea (Johansson, 1896). 25 mm long, uniformly brown, posterior sucker ringed by 10 ocelli and not much broader than anterior sucker and abdomen. Dorsally on *Cottus scorpius.* W. Sweden, Greenland.

Ottoniobdella scorpii (Malm, 1863; Moore and Meyer, 1951). 30 mm long, with longitudinally elongated markings on body, posterior sucker ringed by 12–14 ocelli and twice as broad as anterior sucker and abdomen. On *Cottus scorpius.* Faroes, Iceland, Greenland, Spitzbergen, Bering Sea.

OXYTONOSTOMA Malm 1863 (Johansson, 1898; Selensky, 1914 and 1915; Moore and Meyer, 1951). Suckers discoid, eyes 0, *numerous small tubercles arranged longitudinally in 6 rows dorsally* and 6 rows or none ventrally, abdomen rounded and ill-defined with 11 pairs pulsatile vesicles, annuli 12–14, coelom typical, diverticula fused with 5 fenestrae, testes 6 pairs.

Oxytonostoma arctica Johansson. 25 mm long, tubercles present ventrally. Greenland, White Sea, Kara Sea, Alaska.

Oxytonostoma typica Malm. 20–30 mm long, tubercles absent ventrally. On *Raia radiata.* W. Sweden, Iceland, Greenland, Alaska.

OZOBRANCHUS de Quatrefages 1832 (Selensky, 1915; McCallum, 1918; Oka, 1927; Sanjeeva Raj, 1954). Anterior sucker small, posterior sucker discoid, trachelosome narrow, abdomen broad with *a pair of finger-shaped branching branchiae on each somite*, annuli 2–3, pulsatile vesicles 0, coelom fairly spacious and not divided into lacunae, diverticula separate, testes 4 pairs. On chelonians and crocodiles.

Ozobranchus margoi de Quatrefages. On *Thalassochelys corticata.* Naples.

PARAPONTOBDELLA Harant (1929). Not clearly distinguished from *Pontobdella.*

PISCICOLA de Blainville 1818 (Harding, 1910; Meyer, 1940). Like *Calliobdella* except eyes 2 pairs, annuli 14, bursa simple.

**Piscicola geometra* (L.). 20–50 mm long, with ocelli and radiating marks on posterior sucker. Brackish as well as fresh water, e.g. on *Cottus scorpius* and *Pleuronectes flesus* in Baltic (Herter, 1935).

Piscicola zebra Moore (1898). On lips of *Petromyzon marinus*. Nova Scotia.

"*Piscicola*" *rectangulata* Levinsen. 20–40 mm long from gills and body of *Gadus* in Arctic seas. Has been removed from this genus (Moore and Meyer, 1951) but not yet assigned to a new one.

PLATYBDELLA Malm 1863 (Johansson, 1898; Leigh-Sharpe, 1916). Suckers discoid, eyes 0–3 pairs, abdomen rounded and ill-defined, annuli 3 (6), *coelom reduced* without pulsatile vesicles, dorsal, lateral or segmental lacunae, *diverticula fused* with 5 fenestrae, testes 5 pairs. Only the first sp. listed below has been fully described but about 7 others have been placed tentatively in this inappropriately named genus.

**Platybdella anarrhichae* (Diesing). 20–30 mm long, eyes 0. Gills and body of *Anarrhichas lupus* and *A. minor*. W. Sweden, North Sea, Bergen, Iceland, Greenland.

Platybdella quadrioculata Malm (1863). Eyes 2, posterior sucker not much broader than oral sucker. *Labrus*. W. Sweden, Greenland.

Platybdella buccalis Nigrelli (1946). Eyes 2, posterior sucker twice as broad as oral sucker. Within mouth of *Macrozoarces americanus*. E. coast U.S.

Platybdella fabricii Malm. Eyes 3, posterior sucker twice as broad as oral sucker, row of 12 protuberances on each side of abdomen. *Cottus scorpius*. Greenland, Spitzbergen.

Platybdella olriki Malm. Eyes 3, posterior sucker not much broader than oral sucker. *Hippoglossus vulgaris*, *Sclerocrangon*, *Hyas*.

PODOBDELLA Diesing (1858). Imperfectly described. Like a *Trulliobdella* reversed antero-posteriorly.

PONTOBDELLA Leach 1815 (Harding, 1910; Hickman, 1941; Ingram, 1957). Suckers cup-shaped, trachelosome ill-defined, body rounded and *studded with numerous large and small tubercles*, annuli very distinct 3, 4 or 5, pulsatile vesicles very inconspicuous, coelom typical, diverticula fused, testes 6 pairs, copulatory area with vector tissue. Several spp.

**Pontobdella muricata* (L.) 100–200 mm long, anterior sucker much wider than trachelosome. Various sp. of *Raia*, *Torpedo* and *Pleuronectes*. W. Europe, Mediterranean, Iceland, Greenland, Spitzbergen.

Pontobdella vosmaeri Apàthy (1888). Anterior sucker not much wider than trachelosome. Mediterranean and Roscoff.

PONTOBDELLINA Harding and Moore 1927. Like *Pontobdella* except that body is sharply divided into slender trachelosome and broad flattened abdomen.

PTEROBDELLA Kaburaki 1921 (Harding and Moore, 1927; Scriban and Autrum, 1928–34). Oral sucker small and deeply cupped, eyes 0, posterior sucker large, *anterior two-thirds of body bears on each side a longitudinally running fin* which is indented opposite the clitellum, annuli 14, diverticula absent, testes 5 pairs, genital openings emerge into a common pore. One sp. from *Trygon* in brackish waters of Chilka Lake.

PTEROBDELLINA Bennike and Bruun 1939. Like *Pterobdella* except oral sucker bears 4–6 papillae on each side, *fins run whole length of body*, genital openings are separate.

Pterobdellina jenseni Bennike and Bruun. 20–40 mm long. On *Raia*. Off Faeroes at depths of more than 400 m.

SANGUINOTHUS de Silva and Burdon-Jones 1961. Suckers well developed, eyes 3 pairs, posterior sucker capable of folding round each side of a fin ray and bearing a ring of ocelli, clitellum constricted, abdomen flattened, annuli 3 (6), *coelom reduced* as in *Platybdella*, *diverticula separate*, ganglia 18 + 1 fused anteriorly, testes 5 pairs.

**Sanguinothus pinnarum* de Silva and Burdon-Jones. 10 mm long, uniformly reddish brown. On fins of *Cottus bubalis*. Anglesey and Isle of Man, U.K.

STIBAROBDELLA Leigh–Sharpe 1925 (Harant 1929). Like *Pontobdella*, with which this should perhaps be united. One sp. from Pacific.

TRACHELOBDELLA Diesing 1850 (=*Scorpaenobdella* Saint-Loup, 1886; Apàthy, 1888; Blanchard, 1894; Oka, 1910 and 1927; Selensky, 1915; Dogiel and Bychowsky, 1934; Ingram, 1957). Like *Calliobdella* except posterior sucker fairly small, deeply cupped and facing posteriorly, abdomen more flattened and so more distinct from trachelosome, bursa without muscular organ. About 12 spp.

Trachelobdella lubrica (Grube). 20–30 mm long, yellow or olive-green with white spots, abdomen 1·5 × breadth of posterior sucker which has radiating markings, trachelosome with 4 pairs of lateral vesicles which are non-pulsatile. From a variety of teleosts. Mediterranean and perhaps Atlantic coasts of Europe.

Trachelobdella nigra (Apàthy). Black, contracted abdomen 2–3 × breadth of posterior sucker. Naples.

TRULLIOBDELLA Brinkman 1948. Suckers small but strong, eyes 9 pairs, posterior sucker with ring of ocelli, abdomen flattened and trachelosome narrow like blade and handle of a paddle, annuli 3 (6), pulsatile vesicles and diverticula absent, testes 5 pairs. One sp. from South Georgia.

Host List

This can serve only as a preliminary guide. It is divided regionally to help when leeches are found apart from hosts. The aim has been no more than to cover the North Atlantic forms, but a few records from elsewhere have been included. Many of the invertebrates may serve merely as substrata for cocoons, but some are truly parasitized (Meyer and Barden 1955).

Arctic Seas

Autrum 1936; Borovitzkaia 1949; Bruun 1938; Johansson 1898; Levinsen 1882; Malm 1863; Meyer and Barden 1955; Moore 1940; Moore and Meyer 1951; Remy 1928; Selensky 1914, 1915, 1927; de Silva and Kabata 1961; Wesenberg-Lund 1926.

Hosts		Leeches
INVERTEBRATES		
Colossendeis sp.		*Johanssonia pantopodum*
Crangon borealis		*Platybdella olriki*
Hyas araneus		*Platybdella olriki*
Mysis oculata		*Mysidobdella oculata*
Nymphon strömii		*Johanssonia pantopodum*
Paralithodes camtschaticus cocoons of		*Notostomobdella cyclostoma*
Sclerocrangon boreas		*Crangonobdella murmanica*
Sclerocrangon boreas		*Platybdella fabricii*
VERTEBRATES		
Anarrhichas lupus		*Johanssonia kolaensis*
Anarrhichas lupus	gills	*Platybdella anarrhichae*
Anarrhichas minor		*Calliobdella nodulifera*
Cottus scorpius	ventrally	*Oceanobdella microstoma*
Cottus scorpius	dorsally	*Ottoniobdella brunnea*
Cottus scorpius		*Ottoniobdella scorpii*
Cottus scorpius		*Platybdella fabricii*
Cottus scorpius		*Platybdella olriki*
Gadus macrocephalus gills		"*Piscicola*" *rectangulata*
Gymnacanthus tricuspis		*Platybdella affinis*
Drepanopsetta platessoides gills		*Arctobdella branchiarum*
Hippoglossus hippoglossoides		*Platybdella hippoglossi*
Hippoglossus vulgaris		*Platybdella olriki*
Hippoglossus pingvis		*Notostomobdella laeve*
Lycodes pallidus		*Platybdella anarrhichae*
Myoxocephalus polyacanthocephalus		"*Piscicola*" *rectangulata*
Platysomatichtys hippoglossoides		*Notostomobdella laeve*
Raia radiata		*Oxytonostoma typica*
Somniosus microcephalus		*Notostomobdella laeve*

TEMPERATE NORTH ATLANTIC

Beneden and Hesse 1863; Bennike and Bruun 1939; Brumpt 1900; Bruun 1938; Herter 1935; Johansson 1898; Knight-Jones 1940; Leigh-Sharpe 1914, 1915, 1916, 1933; Malm 1863; Meyer 1940, 1941; Moore 1898, 1946; Nigrelli 1946; Scott 1901; de Silva and Burdon-Jones 1961.

Hosts	Leeches
INVERTEBRATES	
Callinectes sapidus	*Myzobdella lugubris*
VERTEBRATES	
Aetobatus freminvillii	*Branchellion ravenelii*
Amphotistius sabinus	*Branchellion ravenelii*
Anarrhichas lupus gills	*Platybdella anarrhichae*
Anarrhichas lupus externally	*Calliobdella nodulifera*
Blennius pholis	*Calliobdella punctata*
Blennius pholis behind pectoral fin	*Oceanobdella blennii*
Callionymus lyra cloaca	*Ganymedebdella cratere*
Chimaera monstrosa	*Calliobdella nodulifera*
Cottus bubalis fin rays	*Sanguinothus pinnarum*
Cottus bubalis body	*Calliobdella punctata*
Cottus scorpius	*Janusion scorpii*
Cottus scorpius	*Oceanobdella microstoma*
Cottus scorpius	*Ottoniobdella brunnea*
Cottus scorpius (in Baltic)	*Piscicola geometra*
Cyclopterus lumpus	*Oceanobdella sexoculata*
Dasyatis hastatus	*Branchellion ravenelii*
Gadus aeglefinus	*Calliobdella nodulifera*
Gadus callarias	*Calliobdella nodulifera*
Gadus callarias	*Oceanobdella sexoculata*
Gadus carbonarius	*Calliobdella nodulifera*
Gadus merlangus	*Calliobdella nodulifera*
Gadus virens	*Calliobdella nodulifera*
Hippoglossus hippoglossoides	*Platybdella hippoglossi*
Hippoglossus vulgaris	*Calliostoma nodulifera*
Labrus bergylta	*Platybdella quadrioculata*
Lophius piscatorius	*Calliobdella lophii*
Macrozoarces americanus mouth	*Platybdella buccalis*
Merluccius merluccius externally	*Calliobdella nodulifera*
Petromyzon marinus	*Piscicola zebra*
Platichthys flesus (in Baltic)	*Piscicola geometra*
Pleuronectes sp.	*Pontobdella muricata*
Raia batis	*Calliobdella nodulifera*
Raia batis	*Pontobdella muricata*

Raia batis	Pterobdellina jenseni
Raia clavata	Branchellion borealis
Raia clavata	Branchellion torpedinis
Raia clavata	Pontobdella muricata
Raia fullonica	Calliobdella nodulifera
Raia lintea	Pterobdellina jenseni
Raia radiata	Oxytonostoma typica
Scophthalmus maximus	Branchellion torpedinis
Squatina squatina	Branchellion torpedinis
Sebastes norvegicus	Calliobdella nodulifera
Solea solea on scales	Hemibdella soleae
Squalus acanthias	Calliobdella nodulifera
Torpedo torpedo	Branchellion torpedinis
Torpedo torpedo	Pontobdella muricata
Trigla gurnardus	Calliostoma nodulifera
Lepidorhombus whiff-iagonis	Calliobdella nodulifera
Zoarces viviparus	Oceanobdella sexoculata

MEDITERRANEAN

Apàthy 1888, 1890; Leigh-Sharpe 1933; Selensky 1931; Sukat-schoff 1914.

Hosts	Leeches
VERTEBRATES	
Arnoglossus laterna	Ichthyobdella bioculata = Cymatobranchus q.v.
Blennius pholis	Trachelobdella lubrica
Coris giofredi	Trachelobdella lubrica
Corvina nigra	Trachelobdella lubrica
Cottus bubalis	Trachelobdella lubrica
Diplodus annularis	Cyrillobdella alcibiades
Diplodus annularis	Trachelobdella lubrica
Gobius niger	Trachelobdella lubrica
Labrus sp.	Branchellion torpedinis
Lophius piscatorius	Calliobdella lophii
Lophius piscatorius	Trachelobdella lubrica
Raia batis	Pontobdella muricata

Raia clavata	*Branchellion torpedinis*
Raia clavata	*Pontobdella muricata*
Rhinobatis thouin	*Branchellion torpedinis*
Rhomboidichthys podas	*Ichthyobdella bioculata*
Rhombus maximus	*Branchellion torpedinis*
Scophthalmus maximus	*Branchellion torpedinis*
Scorpaena porcus gills or ventrally	*Trachelobdella lubrica*
Scorpaena porcus gills or ventrally	*Trachelobdella nigra*
Scorpaena scrofa	*Trachelobdella lubrica*
Solea impar	*Hemibdella soleae*
Solea hispida	*Hemibdella soleae*
Solea vulgaris	*Hemibdella soleae*
Solea vulgaris	*Trachelobdella lubrica*
Squatina sp. gills	*Ichthyobdella bioculata*
Thalassochelys corticata	*Ozobranchus margoi*
Torpedo marmorata	*Branchellion torpedinis*
Torpedo marmorata	*Pontobdella muricata*
Torpedo ocellata	*Pontobdella muricata*
Trachurus trachurus	*Trachelobdella lubrica*
Trigla sp.	*Ichthyobdella semicoeca*
Trygon pastinaca	*Branchellion torpedinis*
Umbrina cirrosa	*Trachelobdella lubrica*
Uranoscopus scaber	*Trachelobdella lubrica*

SOUTHERN OCEAN AND TEMPERATE PACIFIC

Badham 1916; Benham 1909; Brinkman 1948; Harding 1922; Hickman 1941; Ingram 1957; Leigh-Sharpe 1916, 1925; Meyer and Barden 1955; Moore 1938, 1952; Murphy 1914; Oka 1910, 1927, 1931, 1933; Richardson 1949, 1950, 1953.

Hosts	*Leeches*
INVERTEBRATES	
Crassostrea gigas	*Ostreobdella kakibir*
Chionecoetes opilio	*Carcinobdella kanibir*
VERTEBRATES	
Callorhynchus milii	*Branchellion parkeri*
Dasyatis sp.	*Branchellion parkeri*

Eptatretus cirrhatus	externally	*Bdellamaris eptatreti*
Leptocephalus conger		*Trachelobdella leptocephali*
Mustelus antarcticus		*Branchellion parkeri*
Parachaenichtys georgianus	mouth	*Cryobdellina bacilliformis*
Parachaenichtys georgianus	head	*Trulliobdella capitis*
Platycephalus bassensis		*"Ichthyobdella" platycephali*
Pristiophorus sp.		*Branchellion parkeri*
Raia sp.		*Pontobdella benhami*
Raia sp.		*Pontobdella tasmanica*
Raia lemprieri		*Branchellion australis*
Raia lemprieri		*Branchellion parkeri*
Raia nasuta		*Branchellion parkeri*
Rhombosolea tapirina	dorsally	*Austrobdella bilobata*
Sillago ciliata	fins	*Austrobdella translucens*
Tetraodon hispidus		*Johanssonia abditovesiculata*
Trematomus hansoni	gills	*Cryobdella levigata*

BIBLIOGRAPHY

AUTRUM, H. (1939) Literatur über Hirudineen. In BRONNS, H. G. *Klassen und Ordnungen des Tierreichs* **4**, III, 4, Hirudineen.

AUTRUM, H. 1958. Hirudinea in Brohmer, Ehrmann and Ulmer, *Die Tierwelt Mitteleuropas*, Leipzig.

AUTRUM, H. and GRAETZ, E. (1934) Vergleichende Untersuchungen zur Verdauungsphysiologie der Egel. I. Die Lipatischen Fermente von *Hirudo* und *Haemopis*. *Z. vergl. Physiol.* **21**, 429–439.

BACQ, Z. M. and COPPÉE, G. (1937) Existe-t-il des nerfs cholinergiques chez les invertébrés? *Ann. Physiol. Physicochim. biol.* **13**, 965–970.

BAHL, K. N. (1947) Excretion in the Oligochaeta. *Biol. Rev.* **22**, 109–147.

BARROW, J. H. (1953) The biology of *Trypanosoma diemyctyli* (Tobey). I. *Trypanosoma diemyctyli* in the leech *Batrachobdella picta* (Verrill). *Trans. Amer. micr. Soc.* **72**, 197–216.

BARROW, J. H. (1958) The biology of *Trypanosoma diemyctyli*, (Tobey). III. Factors influencing the cycle of *Trypanosoma diemyctyli* in the vertebrate host *Triturus v. viridescens*. *J. Protozool.* **5**, 161–170.

BENNIKE, S. A. B. (1943) Contributions to the ecology and biology of the Danish freshwater leeches. *Fol. Limnol. Scand.* **2**, 1–109.

BENNIKE, S. A., BOISEN, and BRUUN, A. F. 1939. *Pterobdellina jenseni* n. subgen. n.sp. a new ichthyobdellid from the North Atlantic. *Vidensk. Medd. dansk naturh. Foren. Kbh.* **103**, 517.

BHATIA, M. L. (1938) On the structure of the nephridia and funnels of the Indian leech *Hirudinaria* with remarks on these organs in *Hirudo*. *Quart. J. micr. Sci.* **81**, 27–80.

BHATIA, M. L. (1941) *Hirudinaria* (The Indian cattle leech). *Indian Zool. Mem.* **3**. Lucknow.

BLAIR, W. N. (1927) Notes on *Hirudo medicinalis*, the medicinal leech, as a British species. *Proc. zool. Soc. Lond.* 999–1002.

BLANCHARD, R. (1896) Hirudineen aus dem Togoland. *Arch. Naturg.* **62 (I)**, 49–53.

BOEHM, G. (1947) Über ein rotfluoreszierende, als Porphyrin anzusehende Substanz in den Augen von *Hirudo medicinalis*. *Experientia Basel* **3**, 241.

BOROVITZKAIA, M. 1949. On parasitic leeches of the family Ichthyobdellidae occurring in the pallial cavity of Cephalopod Mollusca *C.R. Acad. Sci. URSS, N.S.* **68** (1), 425–7.

BOYCOTT, A. E. (1936) The habitats of fresh-water Mollusca in Britain. *J. Anim. Ecol.* **5**, 116–186.

BRACONNIER-FAYEMENDY, M. (1933) Sur l'excrétion minérale de la sangsue. *C.R. Soc. Biol., Paris* **114**, 705–706.

BRADBURY, S. (1956) A histochemical study of the adipose cell of the leech *Glossiphonia complanata*. *Quart. J. micr. Sci.* **97**, 499–517.

BRADBURY, S. (1957) A histochemical study of the pigment cells of the leech *Glossiphonia complanata*. *Quart. J. micr. Sci.* **98**, 301–314.

BRADBURY, S. (1958) A cytological and histochemical study of the connective-tissue fibres of the leech *Hirudo medicinalis*. *Quart. J micr. Sci.* **99**, 131–142.

BRADBURY, S. and MEEK, G. A. (1958) The fine structure of the adipose cell of the leech *Glossiphonia complanata*. *J. biophys. biochem. Cytol.* **4**, 603–608.

BRADBURY, S. (1959) The botryoidal and vaso-fibrous tissue of the leech *Hirudo medicinalis*. *Quart. J. micr. Sci.* **100**, 483–498.

BRAND, T. von, (1946) *Anaerobiosis in Invertebrates*, Missouri.

BRINKMAN, A., Jr. 1948. Some new and remarkable leeches from the Antarctic Seas. *Sci. Res. Norweg. Antarct. Exped.* 1927–28, Oslo No. 29, 1–17.

BRISTOL, C. (1898) The metamerism of *Nephelis*. A contribution to the morphology of the nervous system with a description of *Nephelis lateralis*. *J. Morphol.* **15**, 17–72.

BRONNS, H. G. (1936–9) *Klassen und Ordnungen des Tierreichs*. 4, Vermes; III, Annelides; 4, Hirudinea. Leipzig.

BROWN, F. A. (1957) The rhythmic nature of life. In SCHEER, B. T. *Recent Advances in Invertebrate Physiology*, Oregon.

BRUMPT, E. (1900) Reproduction des Hirudinées. *Mém. Soc. zool. France* **13**, 286–430.

BUDDENBROCK, W. von (1953) *Vergleichende Physiologie*. 2. Nervenphysiologie. Basel.

BÜRGER, O. (1891) Beiträge zur Entwicklungsgeschichte der Hirudineen. Zur Embryologie von *Nephelis*. *Zool. Jb. Anat.* **4**, 697–783.

BÜRGER, O. (1902) Weitere Beiträge zur Entwicklungsgeschichte der Hirudineen. Zur Embryologie von *Clepsine*. *Z. wiss. Zool.* **72**, 525–544.

BÜSING, K. H. (1951) *Pseudomonas hirudinis* ein bakterieller Darmsymbiont des Blutegels (*Hirudo medicinalis*). *Zbl. Bakt. (I. Abt. Orig.)* **157**, 478.

BÜSING, K. H., DÖLL, W. and FREYTAG, K. (1953) Die Bakterienflora der medizinischen Blutegel. *Arch. Mikrobiol.* **19**, 52–86.

BYCHOWSKY, A. (1921) Über die Entwicklung der Nephridien von *Clepsine sexoculata* Bergm. (= *compl.* Sav.). Ein Beitrag zum Nephridialproblem. *Rev. Suisse Zool.* **29**, 41–131.

CABALLERO, E. 1956. Hirudineos de Mexico XX Taxa y nomenclatura de la Clase Hirudinea hasta generos. *Ann. Inst. Biol. Univ. Mex.* **27**, 279–302.

CASTLE, W. E. (1900) The metamerism of the Hirudinea. *Proc. Amer. Acad. Arts. Sci.* **35**, 285–303.

CHAPMAN, G. (1958) The hydrostatic skeleton in the invertebrates. *Biol. Rev.* **33**, 338–371.

CHILD, C. M. (1900) The early development of *Arenicola* and *Sternaspis*. *Arch. EntwMech. Org.* **9**, 587–722.

CLARK, R. B. and COWEY, J. B. (1958) Factors controlling the change of shape of certain nemertean and turbellarian worms. *J. exp. Biol.* **35**, 731–748.

CORDIER, R. (1934) Études histophysiques sur la nephridie du Lombric. *Arch. biol.* **45**, 431–471.

COHEN, S. and LEWIS, H. (1949) The nitrogen metabolism of the earthworm. *J. biol. Chem.* **180**, 79–91.

CUENOT, L. (1931) La fonction athrocytaire chez les Hirudinées. *C.R. Acad. Sci. Paris*, **193**, 626–629.

DAWYDOFF, C. (1959) Ontogenèse des annélides. In GRASSÉ, P. *Traité de Zoologie* 5 (I). Paris.

DENZER-MELBRANDT, U. (1935) Helligkeits- und Farbensinn bei deutschen Süsswasseregeln. *Zool. Jb. Physiol.* **55**, 525–562.

DIMPKER, A. M. (1917) Die Eifurchung von *Herpobdella atomaria* Carena. (*Nephelis vulgaris* Moqu.-Tand.) *Zool. Jb. Anat.* **40**, 245–290.

DIWANY, H. EL (1925) Récherches expérimentales sur l'histophysiologie comparée de l'appareil digestif des invertébrés hématophages. I. Les Hirudinées. *Arch. Anat. Hist. Embryol.* **4**, 229–258.

EMDEN, M. van (1929) Bau und Function des Botryoidgewebes von *Herpobdella atomaria* Carena. *Z. wiss. Zool.* **134**, 1–83.

FLORKIN, M. (1935) Où en est la Biochimie comparée? *Ann. Bull. Soc. Roy. Sci. Med. Nat. Bruxelles* 9–10.

FLORKIN, M. (1949) *Biochemical Evolution*, New York.

GASKELL, J. F. (1919) Adrenalin in annelids. *J. gen. Physiol.* **2**, 73–85.

GEE, W. (1912) The behaviour of leeches with especial reference to its modifiability. *Univ. Calif. Publ. Zool.* **2**, 197–305.

GOODRICH, E. S. (1945) The study of nephridia and genital ducts since 1895. *Quart. J. micr. Sci.* **86**, 113–392.

GRAETZ, E. and AUTRUM, H. (1935) Vergleichende Untersuchungen zur Verdauungsphysiologie der Egel. II. Die fermente der Eiweissverdauung bei *Hirudo* und *Haemopis*. *Z. vergl. Physiol.* **22**, 273–283.

GRASSÉ, P. (1959) *Traité de Zoologie* 5 (I). Paris.

GRATIOLET, P. (1862) Recherches sur l'organisation du système vasculaire dans la sangsue médicinale et l'aulastome vorace. *Ann. Sci. nat.* (*Zool.*) **17**, 174–225.

GRAY, J., LISSMAN, H. W. and PUMPHREY, R. J. (1938) The mechanism of locomotion in the leech (*Hirudo medicinalis*). *J. exp. Biol.* **15**, 408–430.

HALL, F. G. (1922) The vital limits of exsiccation of certain animals. *Biol. Bull.* **42**, 31–51.

HARDING, W. A. (1910) A revision of the British leeches. *Parasitology* **3**, 130–201.

HAVET, J. (1900) Structure du système nerveux des annélides *Nephelis*, *Clepsine*, *Hirudo*, *Lumbriculus*, *Lumbricus* (Methode de Golgi). *Cellule* **17**, 65–137.

HAYCRAFT, J. B. (1884) On the action of a secretion obtained from the medicinal leech on the coagulation of the blood. *Proc. Roy. Soc.* **36**, 478–487.

HEIDERMANNS, C. (1937) Excretion und Excretstoffwechsel der Wirbellosen. *Tab. Biol.* **14**, 209–273.

HERTER, K. (1928a) Reizphysiologische Untersuchungen an dem Egel *Hemiclepsis marginata* O. F. Müller. *Verh. Dtsch. Zool. Ges.* **32**, 154–160.

HERTER, K. (1928b) Bewegungsphysiologische Studien an dem Egel *Hemiclepsis marginata* O. F. Müller mit besonderer Berucksichtigung der Thermokinese. *Z. vergl. Physiol.* **7**, 571–605.

HERTER, K. (1928c) Reizphysiologie und Wirtsfindung des Fischegels *Hemiclepsis marginata* O. F. Müller. *Z. vergl. Physiol.* **8**, 391–444.

HERTER, K. (1929a) Über Geotaxis und Phototaxis deutscher Egel. *Verh. Dtsch. Zool. Ges.* **33**, 72–82.

HERTER, K. (1929b) Vergleichende bewegungsphysiologische Studien an deutschen Egeln. *Z. vergl. Physiol.* **9**, 145–177.

HERTER, K. (1929c) Temperatureversuche mit Egeln. *Z. vergl. Physiol.* **10**, 248–271.

HERTER, K. (1929d) Reizphysiologisches Verhalten und Parasitismus des Entenegels *Protoclepsis tesselata* O. F. Müll. *Z. vergl. Physiol.* **10**, 272–308.

HERTER, K. (1929e) Studien über Reizphysiologie und Parasitismus bei Fisch-und Entenegeln. *SB. Ges. Naturf. Fr. Berlin* 142–184.

HERTER, K. (1932) *Hirudinea*, Egel. In SCHULZE, P. *Biologie der Tiere Deutschlands* **12b** (35) 1–158.

HERTER, K. (1936) Die Physiologie der Hirudineen. In BRONNS, H. G. *Klassen und Ordnungen des Tierreichs* 4, III, 4; 123–319.

HERTER, K. (1937) Die Ökologie der Hirudineen. In BRONNS, H. G. *Klassen und Ordnungen des Tierreichs*, 4, III, 4; 321–496.

HERTER, K. (1942) Untersuchungen über den Temperatursinn von Warmbluten Parasiten. *Z. Parasitenk.* **12**, 552–591.

HESS, W. N. (1925) Reactions to light in the earthworm *Lumbricus terrestris*. *J. Morph. Physiol.* **39**, 515–542.

HESSE, R. (1897) Untersuchungen über die Organe der Lichtempfindung bei niederen Tieren. III. Die Sehorgane der Hirudineen. *Z. wiss. Zool.* **62**, 671–707.

HICKMAN, V. V. 1941. A new Ichthyobdellid leech and its egg capsules. *Pap. roy. Soc. Tasm.* (1941). 41–44.

HIESTAND, W. A. and SINGER, T. I. (1934) Certain factors influencing the respiratory metabolism of the leech (*Hirudo medicinalis*) *Proc. Indiana Acad. Sci.* **43**, 205–210.

HOFFMANN, J. (1955) Quelques caractères éthologiques de la Piscicolidée: *Cystobranchus respirans* Troschel. *Arch. Inst. Grand-Ducal Luxemb. Sect. Sci. nat. phys. math.* **22**, 223–225.

HOFFMANN, J. (1956) Contributions à l'étude des spécificités morphologiques et éthologiques de la Piscicolidée: *Cystobranchus respirans* Troschel, 1850. *Arch. Inst. Grand-Ducal Luxemb. Sect. Sci. nat. phys. math*, **23**, 209–239.

HOLMES, S. J. (1905) The selection of random movement as a factor in phototaxis. *J. comp. Neurol.* **15**, 98–112.

HORRIDGE, G. A. and ROBERTS, M. B. V. (1960) Neuro–muscular transmission in the earthworm. *Nature* **186**, 650.

HYMAN, L. H. (1929) The effect of oxygen tension on oxygen consumption in *Planaria* and some echinoderms. *Physiol. Zool.* **2**, 505–534.

INGRAM, D. M. 1957. Some Tasmanian Hirudinea. *Pap. roy. Soc. Tasm.* **91**, 191–232.

ITO, T. (1936) Cytology of ganglion cells in the ventral nerve cord of *Hirudo nipponica*. *Folio Anat. Japon.* **14**, 389–412.

IWATA, K. S. (1940a) Spreading of action potential in the skin of a leech. *Japan. J. Zool.* **8**, 433–441.

IWATA, K. S. (1940b) Seat of action potential in the skin of the leech. *Japan. J. Zool.* **8**, 443–447.

JASCHKE, W. (1933) Beiträge zur Kenntnis der symbiontischen Einrichtungen bei Hirudineen und Ixodiden. *Z. Parasitenk.* **5**, 515–541.

JOHNSON, M. L. (1942) The respiratory function of the haemoglobin of the earthworm. *J. exp. Biol.* **18**, 266–277.

JUNG, T. (1955) Zur Kenntnis der Ernährungsbiologie der in dem Raum zwischen Harz und Heide vorkommenden Hirudineen. *Zool. J. (Allg. Zool.)* **66**, 79–128.

KABURAKI, T. (1921) Notes on some leeches in the collection of the Indian Museum. *Rec. Ind. Mus.* **18**, 689–719.

KAISER, F. (1954) Beitrage zur Bewegungsphysiologie der Hirudineen. *Zool. Jb. (Allg. Zool.)* **65**, 59–90.

KLEKOWSKI, R. (1961) Die Resistenz gegen Austrocknung bei einigen Wirbellosen aus astatischen Gewassern. *Verh. int. Ver. Limnol.* **14**, (In press).

KNIGHT-JONES, E. W. 1940. The occurrence of a marine leech, *Abranchus blennii* n. sp., resembling *A. sexoculatus* (Malm) in North Wales. *J. Mar. biol. Ass. U.K.* **24**, 533–541.

KOWALEVSKI, A. (1900) Etude biologique de l'*Haementeria costata* Müller. *Mem. Ac. Sci. St. Petersb.* (8) **11**, 1–77.

KROGH, A. (1939) *Osmotic Regulation in Aquatic Animals*. Cambridge.

LANKESTER, E. R. (1880) On the connective and vasifactive tissue of the medicinal leech. *Quart. J. micr. Sci.* (*N.S.*) **20**, 307–317.

LAPICQUE, L. and VEIL, C. (1925) Vitesse de la conduction nerveuse et musculaire comparée à la chronaxie chez la sangsue et le ver de terre. *C.R. Soc. Biol. Paris* **93**, 1590–1591.

LENGGENHAGER, K. (1936) Das Ratsel des Blutegelbisses. *Schweiz. med. Wschr.* **9**, 227–228.

LEOPOLDSEDER, F. (1931) Entwicklung des Eies von *Clepsine* nach Entfernung des vegetativen Polplasmas. *Z. wiss. Zool.* **139**, 201–248.

LESLIE, C. J. (1951) Mating behaviour of leeches. *J. Bombay nat. Hist. Soc.* **50**, 422–423.

LEUCKART, R. and BRANDES, G. (1886–1901) *Die parasiten des Menschen.* I (2), 535–897. Leipzig.

LINDEMAN, V. F. (1932) Respiratory regulation in the leech (*Hirudo medicinalis*). *Physiol. Zool.* **5**, 560–565.

LINDEMAN, V. F. (1935) The relation of temperature to respiratory regulation in the leech (*Hirudo medicinalis*). *Physiol. Zool.* **8**, 311.

LINDEMANN, B. (1939) Das Verhalten der Kapillaren in der Umgebung des Blutegelbisses. *Arch. exp. Path. Pharmak.* **193**, 490–502.

LIVANOW, N. (1904) Untersuchungen zur Morphologie der Hirudineen. II. Das Nervensystem des Vorderen Körperendes und seine Metamerie. *Zool. Jb.* (*Anat.*) **20**, 153–226.

LIVANOW, N. (1906) *Acanthobdella peledina* Grube, 1851. *Zool. Jb.* (*Anat.*) **22**, 637–866.

LÖHNER, L. (1916) Über geschmacksphysiologische Versuche mit Blutegeln. *Pflügers Arch.* **163**, 239–246.

LUKIN, E. I. (1957) On the distribution of the medicinal leech in the U.S.S.R. *Zool. Zh.* **36**, 658–669.

MACCALLUM, W. G. and MACCALLUM, G. A. (1918) On the anatomy of *Ozobranchus branchiatus* (Menzies). *Bull. Amer. Mus. Nat. Hist.* **38**, 295–408.

MAIER, B. L. (1892) Beiträge zur Kenntniss des Hirudineen-Auges. *Zool. Jb. Anat.* **5**, 552–580.

MANN, K. H. (1951) On the bionomics and distribution of *Theromyzon tessulatum* (O. F. Müller, 1774) (= *Protoclepsis tesselata*). *Ann. Mag. nat. Hist.* **4**, 956–961.

MANN, K. H. (1953a) The segmentation of leeches. *Biol. Rev.* **28**, 1–15.

MANN, K. H. (1953b) The life history of *Erpobdella octoculata* (L.) *J. anim. Ecol.* **22**, 199–207.

MANN, K. H. (1955) The ecology of the British freshwater leeches. *J. anim. Ecol.* **24**, 98–119.

MANN, K. H. (1956) A study of the oxygen consumption of five species of leech. *J. exp. Biol.* **33**, 615–626.

MANN, K. H. (1957a) A study of a population of the leech *Glossiphonia complanata* (L.). *J. anim. Ecol.* **26**, 99–111.

MANN, K. H. (1957b) The breeding, growth and age structure of a population of the leech *Helobdella stagnalis* (L.). *J. anim. Ecol.* **26**, 171–177.

MANN, K. H. (1958) Seasonal variation in the respiratory acclimatisation of the leech *Erpobdella testacea* (Sav.). *J. exp. Biol.* **35**, 314–323.

MANN, K. H. (1961) The oxygen requirements of leeches considered in relation to their habitats. *Verh. int. Ver. Limnol.* **14**, (In press).

MANN, K. H. (1961) The life history of the leech *Erpobdella testacea* and its adaptive significance. *Oikos* 12, 164–169.

MANNSFELD, W. (1934) Zur Kenntnis der Hirudineenfauna Lettlands. *Korr. bl. Natf.-Ver. Riga* 61, 156–167.

MATHERS, C. K. 1954. *Haemopis kingi*, new species (Annelida, Hirudinea). *Amer. Midl. Nat.* 52, 460–468.

MATTHEWS, R. S. (1954) Land leeches. *J. Bombay nat. Hist. Soc.* 52, 655–656.

MEYER, M. C. 1940. A revision of the leeches living on freshwater fishes of North America. *Trans. Amer. micr. Soc.* 59 (3), 354–376.

MEYER, M. C. 1941. The rediscovery together with the morphology of the leech *Branchellion ravenelii*. *J. Parasitol.* 27, 289–298.

MEYER, M. C. 1946. A new leech *Piscicola salmositica*. *J. parasitol.* 32, 467–476.

MEYER, M. C. and BARDEN, A. A. 1955. Leeches symbiotic on Arthropoda, especially decapod Crustacea. *Wasmann J. Biol.* 13, 297–311.

MEYER, M. C. and MOORE, J. P. 1954. Notes on Canadian leeches (Hirudinea) with the description of a new species. *Wasmann J. Biol.* 12, 63–96.

MILLER, J. A. (1942) Studies in the biology of the leech. 5. Behaviour following nerve cord transection. *Ohio J. Sci.* 42, 45–52.

MILLER, J. A. (1945) Studies in the biology of the leech. 9. The gross nervous system. *Ohio J. Sci.* 45, 233–246.

MINZ, B. (1932) Pharmakologische Untersuchungen am Blutegel-präparat, zugleich eine Methode zum biologischen Nachweis von Acetylcholin bei Anwesenheit anderer pharmakologisch wirksamer körpereigener Stoffe. *Arch. exp. Path.* 168, 292–304.

MOORE, J. P. (1900) A description of *Microbdella biannulata* with especial regard to the constitution of the leech somite. *Proc. Ac. nat. Sci. Philad.* 5, 50–73.

MOORE, J. P. 1940. *Austrobdella anoculata*, a new species of fish leech from Greenland, *J. Wash. Acad. Sci.* 30, 520.

MOORE, J. P. 1946. The anatomy and systematic position of *Myzobdella lugubris* Leidy. *Notul. nat. Acad. Philad.* 184, 1.

MOORE, J. P. 1947. See footnote in: Kenk, R. Animal life of temporary and permanent ponds in southern Michigan. *Misc. Pub. Mus. Zool. Univ. Michigan.* 71, 1–66.

MOORE, J. P. 1952. New Piscicolidae from the Pacific and their anatomy. *Occ. Pap. Bishop Mus.* 21 (2), 17–44.

MOORE, J. P. 1953. Three undescribed North American leeches (Hirudinea). *Notul. nat. Acad. Philad.* 250, 1–13.

MOORE, J. P. and MEYER, M. C. 1951. Leeches (Hirudinea) from Alaska and adjacent waters. *Wasmann J. Biol.* 9, 11–77.

MÜLLER, K. J. (1932) Über normale Entwicklung, inverse Asymmetrie und Doppelbildungen bei *Clepsine sexoculata*. *Z. wiss. Zool.* 142, 425–490.

MURNAGHAN, M. F. (1958) The morphinized-eserinized leech muscle for the assay of acetylcholine. *Nature* **182**, 317.

NAGAO, Z. (1957) Observations on the breeding habits in a freshwater leech *Herpobdella lineata* O. F. Müller. *J. Fac. Sci. Hokkaido* **(VI)** **13**, 192–196.

NAGAO, Z. (1958) Some observations on the breeding habits of a freshwater leech *Glossiphonia lata* Oka. *Jap. J. Zool.* **12**, 219–228.

NIGRELLI, R. F. 1946. Studies on the marine resources of southern New England. V. Parasites and diseases of the ocean pout *Macrozoarces americanus*, III *Platybdella buccalis* sp. n. an Ichthyobdellid leech from the mouth. *Bull. Bingham oceanogr. Coll.* **9**, 215.

NYBELIN, O. 1943. *Nesophilemon* n.g. für *Philaemon skottsbergi* L. Johansson aus den Juan Fernandez Iseln. *Zool. Anz.* **142**, 249–250.

OHLE, W. (1934) Chemische und physicalische Untersuchungen norddeutscher Seen. *Arch. Hydrobiol. Plankt.* **26**, 386–464.

OKA, A. (1894) Beitrage zur Anatomie der *Clepsine*. *Z. wiss. Zool.* **58**, 79–151.

OKA, A. (1922) Hirudinea from the Inlé Lake, S. Shan States. *Rec. Ind. Mus.* **24**, 521–534.

OZER, F. and WINTERSTEIN, H. (1949) Über die Beziehung zwisches Sauerstoffverbrauch und Kontraktion beim Blutmuskel. *Physiol. comp. Oecol. Den. Haag.* I, 331–339.

PAWLOWSKI, L. K. (1936) Zur Okologie der Hirudineen-fauna der Wigryseen. *Arch. Hydrobiol. Rybact.* **10**, 1–47.

PAWLOWSKI, L. K. (1955) Observations biologiques sur les sangsues. *Bull. Soc. Sci. Lettr. Lódź* (III), **6**, 1–21.

PAWLOWSKI, L. K. 1955. Revision des genres *Erpobdella* de Blainville et *Dina* Blanchard (Hirudinea). *Bull. Soc. Sci. Lódź.* **6**, 1–15.

PENNERS, A. (1923) Die Entwicklung bei Keimstreife und die Organbildung bei *Tubifex*. *Zool. Jb. Anat.* **43**, 323–368.

PEREZ, H. V. Z. (1942) On the chromaffin cells in the nerve ganglion of *Hirudo*. *J. comp. Neurol.* **76**, 367–401.

PÜTTER, A. (1907) Der Stoffwechsel der Blutegels (*Hirudo medicinalis*). 1. *Z. allg. Physiol.* **6**, 217–286.

PÜTTER, A. (1908) Der Stoffwechsel der Blutegels (*Hirudo medicinalis*). 2. *Z. allg. Physiol.* **7**, 16–61.

RAMSAY, J. (1949a) The osmotic relations of the earthworm. *J. exp. Biol.* **26**, 46–56.

RAMSAY, J. (1949b) The site of formation of hypotonic urine in the nephridium of *Lumbricus*. *J. exp. Biol.* **26**, 65–75.

REICHENOW, E. (1922) Intracellular Symbionten bei blutsaugenden Milben und Egeln. *Arch. Protistenk.* **45**, 95–116.

RETZIUS, G. (1891) Zur Kenntnis des centralen Nervensystems der Würmer. *Biol. Unters.* (N.F.), **2**, 1–28.

RICHARDSON, L. R. 1949. Studies on New Zealand Hirudinea II, *Branchellion parkeri*, a new Ichthyobdellid leech. *Zool. Pub. Vict.* *N.Z* **1**, 1–11.

RICHARDSON, L. R. 1950. Studies on New Zealand Hirudinea. I. *Pontobdella benhami* n. sp. *Trans. Roy. Soc. N.Z.* **78** (1), 97–100.

RICHARDSON, L. R. 1953. Studies on New Zealand Hirudinea. Part III. *Bdellamaris eptatreti* n.g., n.sp. and notes on other Piscicolidae. *Trans. Roy. Soc. N.Z.* **81**(2), 283–294.

RINGUELET, R. 1945. Hirudineos del Museo de la Plata. *Rev. Mus. Plata Zool.* (N.S.) **4**, 95–137.

RINGUELET, R. 1954. La classification de los hirudineos. *Notas Mus. Plata Zool.* **16**, 257–272.

ROBIN, Y., van THOAI, N. and PRADEL, L.-A. (1957) Metabolism des dérivés guanidylés. VII. Sur une nouvelle guanidine monosubtituée biologique: L'hirudonine. *Biochim. Biophys. Acta.* **24**, 381–384.

ROOTS, B. I. (1960) Some observations on the chloragogenous tissue of earthworms. *Comp. Biochem. Physiol.* **1**, 218–226.

SANDNER, H. (1951) Badania nad Fauna Pijawek. *Acta Zool. Oecol. Univ. Lódz.* **4**, 1–50.

SANJEEVA RAJ, P. J. 1954. A synopsis of the species of the genus *Ozobranchus*. *J. Bombay nat. Hist. Soc.* **52**, 473–480.

SCHLUTER, E. (1933) Die Bedeutung des Centralnervensystems von *Hirudo medicinalis* für Locomotion und Raumorientierung. *Z. wiss. Zool.* **143**, 538–593.

SCHMIDT, G. A. (1917) Zur Entwicklung des Entoderms bei *Protoclepsis tesselata*. *Ann. zool. Abteil. Ges. Freunde N.A.u.E.*, **4** (N.S.), Moscow.

SCHMIDT, G. A. (1944) Adaptive significance of peculiarities of the cleavage process in leeches. *J. Gen. Biol. Moscow* **5**, 284–303.

SCHOUMKINE, O. B. (1953) Embryonic development of *Hirudo*. *Trud. Inst. Morf. Zhiv.* **8**, 216–279.

SCHWAB, A. (1949) Über die Nerven- und Muskelphysiologie des Pferdegels *Haemopis sanguisuga*. *Z. vergl. Physiol.* **31**, 506–526.

SCIACCHITANO, I. 1939. Nuovi irudinei del Congo Belga. *Rev. Zool. Bot. Afric.* **32**, 348–367.

SCIACCHITANO, I. 1941. Le attuali conoscenze sugli irudinei dell' Africa italiana. *Riv. Biol. Colon.* **14**, 161–170.

SCRIBAN, I. A. and AUTRUM, H. (1932–34) Ordnung der Clitellata: Hirudinea = Egel. In KUKENTHAL, W. and KRUMBACH, T., *Handbuch der Zoologie* **2** (8), 119–352.

SEMAL- VAN GANSEN, P. (1956) Les cellules chlorogogenes des lombriciens. *Bull. Biol. France–Belg.* **90**, 335–356.

de SILVA, P. H. D. H. and BURDON-JONES, C. 1961. A new genus and species of leech parasitic on *Cottus bubalis*. *Proc. zool. Soc. Lond.* **136**, 343–357.

de SILVA, P. H. D. H. and KABATA, Z. 1961. A new genus and species of leech parasitic on *Drepanopsetta platessoides* (Malm) the long rough dab. *Proc. zool. Soc. Lond.* **136**, 331–341.

SMITH, R. I. (1942) Nervous control of chromatophores in the leech *Placobdella parasitica*. *Physiol. Zool.* **15**, 410–417.

STAMMERS, F. M. G. (1950) Observations on the behaviour of land leeches. *Parasitology* **40**, 237–245.

STEPHENSON, J. (1930) *The Oligochaeta* Oxford.

SUKATSCHOFF, B. (1903) Beiträge zur Entwicklungsgeschichte der Hirudineen. II. Über die Furchung und Bildung der embryonalen Anlagen bei *Nephelis vulgaris* Moqu.-Tand. (*Herpobdella atomaria*). *Z. wiss. Zool.* **73**, 321–367.

SUKATSCHOFF, B. (1912) Beiträge zur Anatomie der Hirudineen. I. Über den Bau von *Branchellion torpedinis* Sav. *Mitt. zool. Stat. Neapel.* **20**, 395–528.

SZIDAT, L. (1930) Beiträge zur Entwicklungsgeschichte der Holostomiden. III. Über zwei Tetra-cotylen aus Hirudineen und ihre Weiterentwicklung in Enten zu *Cotylurus cornutus* Rud. und *Apatemon gracilis* Rud. *Zool. Anz.* **86**, 133–149.

TERIO, B. (1950) Sulla presenza di reti nervose diffuse nel tratta pharyngogastrico di *Hirudo medicinalis*. *Boll. zool.* **17**, 25–27.

TILLOY, R. (1937) La fonction athrocytaire chez les Hirudinées (essai d'explication de la sélection des colorants). *Bull. mém. Soc. Sci. Nancy.* (*N.S.*) **7**, 199–225.

TUCKER, D. S. (1958) The distribution of some freshwater invertebrates in ponds in relation to annual fluctuations in the chemical composition of the water. *J. anim. Ecol.* **27**, 105–123.

VAVROUSKOVA, K. (1952) Farbwechsel des Egels *Protoclepsis tesselata* O.F. Müller. *Mém. Soc. zool. tchéosl.* **16**, 334–353.

WADDINGTON, C. H. (1956) *Principles of Embryology* London.

WELLS, G. P. (1932) Colour response in a leech. *Nature* **129**, 686–687.

WENDROWSKY, V. (1928) Über die Chromosomencomplexe der Hirudineen. *Z. Zellforsch.* **8**, 153–175.

WHITMAN, C. O. (1878) The embryology of *Clepsine*. *Quart. J. micr. Sci.* **18**, 215–315.

WHITMAN, C. O. (1886) The leeches of Japan. *Quart. J. micr. Sci.* (*N.S.*) **26**, 317–416.

WIGGLESWORTH, V. B. (1953) *The Principles of Insect Physiology* 5th ed. London.

WILSON, D. P. (1932) Development of *Nereis pelagica*. *J. Mar. biol. Ass. U.K.* **18**, 203–217.

WILSON, D. M. (1960) Nervous control of movements in annelids. *J. exp. Biol.* **37**, 46–56.

WINTERSTEIN, H. and OZER, F. (1949) Osmotische Druck und Ionengleichgewicht beim Blutegelmuskel. *Z. vergl. Physiol.* **31**, 308–321.

WORTH, C. B. (1951) Description and discussion of the biting of an Indian land leech. *J. Bombay nat. Hist. Soc.* **50**, 423–426.

YANAGISAWA, H. and YOKOI, E. (1938) The purification of *Hirudin* and action principle of *Hirudo medicinalis*. *Proc. imp. Acad. Tokyo* 14.

ZICK, K. (1933) Weiteres über Zucht und Fortpflanzung des Medizinischen Blutegels. *Zool. Anz.* **103** 49–55.

INDEX

(Italics indicate illustrations)

As the Appendixes A and B are arranged for easy reference they are not covered by the index